My Quran Friends

STORYBOOK

**Learning with Friends
from the Quran and Today**

First published 2006
© Goodword Books 2006
Illustrated by Gurmeet

Goodword Books Pvt. Ltd.
P. O. Box No. 3244, Nizamuddin West,
New Delhi-110 013
info@goodwordbooks.com
Printed in India

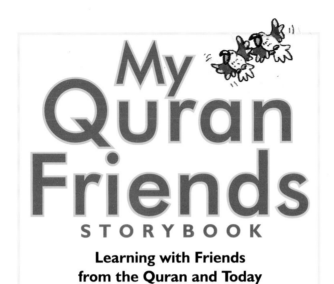

My Quran Friends

STORYBOOK

**Learning with Friends
from the Quran and Today**

Saniyasnain Khan
Vinni Rahman

GOODWORD

www.goodwordbooks.com

CONTENTS

Quran Friends

Friends of Today

Quran Friends

Are you ready to hear exciting stories from the Quran? Quran friends love Allah and want to do what He says, and the best way to learn is to listen to Allah's Word, the Quran. So join the Quran friends and read these stories of Quran friends. You will be off to an exciting learning experience.

The Pride of Satan

Allah created Adam, the first man, from dry clay and breathed His spirit into him, which made him superior to all other creations. Allah ordered the angels to bow down, and all of them did so except Satan. He was of those who reject faith. Allah asked Satan, "Why do you not bow down?" Satan replied, "I will not bow to a mortal created of dry clay."

"Get away from here!" commanded Allah. "You are accursed. My curse shall be on you till Judgement Day." "Allah," begged Satan, "give me then respite till the Day of Resurrection." "You are granted respite till the Appointed Day," agreed Allah. "Allah you have made me commit a sin. Now I will make wrong appear like right to man and put all in the wrong like me." Allah agreed and said, "But you shall have no power over My true servants, only the sinners will follow you to Hell." Satan's arrogance and self-love were the root of evil and unbelief. This made him disobey Allah's command and rebel against Him. He could not even see his own fault and blamed Allah for leading him into sin.

Talk with me

What did Allah ask the angels to do?
Why did Iblis not obey Allah's command?

Say with me

And when We said to the angels: 'Prostrate yourselves before Adam,' they all prostrated themselves except Satan, who in his pride refused and became an unbeliever. (2:34)

Pray with me

Dear Allah, save us from pride, arrogance and self-love from which all sins come.

Two Brothers

The Prophet Adam ﷺ and Hawwa(Eve) had two sons, Habil(Abel) and Qabil(Cain). Habil was humble and Qabil was arrogant. One day they made offerings to Allah. Habil, the shepherd, took the best of his flocks and Qabil, the farmer, brought the best of his crops. Habil's offering was accepted but Qabil's was rejected.

Qabil's pride was hurt because his offering was rejected and his brother's was accepted. He became jealous and angry with his brother and blamed him for his disgrace. Habil tried to set him right and said, "If your sacrifice was not accepted there was something wrong in you, for Allah is just and accepts the sacrifice of the righteous. You are proud and have no fear of Allah." But Qabil refused to see his own mistake. Instead he disagreed and shouted, "Now I will kill you!" Habil did not want to fight and replied, "I am not going to fight back, though I am as strong as you are, because I fear Allah. Let me warn you that you are committing a sin and for it you will suffer in hell."

Habil's words had no effect on Qabil, as anger had blinded him and he couldn't see what was right or wrong. In his pride, jealousy and anger, he killed Habil, his brother, and thereby earned Allah's displeasure.

Talk with me

Why was Qabil's offering not accepted?

Why did Qabil kill Habil?

Say with me

If anyone killed a person – except as a punishment for murder or other corruption in the land, it shall be as if he had killed the whole of humanity. And whoever saved a human life shall be looked upon as if he had saved all mankind. (5:32)

Pray with me

Dear Allah, protect us from pride, jealousy and anger and guide us to love and respect the whole of humanity

The Great Flood

The children of Adam and Hawwa worshipped Allah and did good deeds. Later, some of them in memory of their dead pious elders started making statues of them. The following generations began to worship these statues, calling them their gods. They forgot Allah and left the correct path taught by their elders. They became wicked and cruel to the poor. Allah sent the Prophet Nuh ﷺ (Noah) to guide them back to the right path. He asked them to mend their ways and seek pardon from Allah. He asked them not to be cruel to poor. He informed them that everyone had to be responsible for their deeds as, on the Day of Judgement, they would be judged by them. Only some poor people listened to him. The rest not only refused to listen to him but even tried to physically harm him. Still he did not give up and prayed to Allah to forgive his people, as they did not know what they were doing.

Finally, the Prophet Nuh ﷺ warned his people of an approaching flood, which would destroy everything on the earth. But they made fun of him and even called him a mad-man. Allah asked him to build an Ark and also guided him how to make it. It took him a long time to complete it. The Prophet Nuh ﷺ and his followers then collected all the species of animals as Allah had ordered them. All the animals, male and female — some with wings and some with legs and some that crawled — were taken aboard in pairs.

Slowly clouds began to cover the sky as the storm drew near. At first it only drizzled, but in no time the rain became so heavy that the whole world grew dark. The Prophet Nuh ﷺ called his people to the Ark: "Embark! In the name of Allah, it shall set sail and cast anchor. My Lord is forgiving and merciful." The son of the Prophet Nuh ﷺ, Kanaan, did not believe in his father's message and refused to come aboard. But his brothers, Shem, Ham, Japheth and other believers did and went on to the Ark along with all the other believers. The Prophet Nuh's wife, Waliya, did not believe in her husband either, and had to be left behind. His unbelieving son and wife were punished for their deeds and were destroyed.

The wind grew stronger, the rain heavier and the storm struck the earth with great force. At Allah's command the floodgates of heaven opened and rain poured down in torrents. Fountains of water came gushing out from cracks in the earth. Soon all the rivers overflowed and water covered every inch of the ground. The passengers of the Ark were terrified by the storm, but they were sure that they would be safe as they had faith in Allah. They kept praying to Allah for His Mercy at this great moment of trial.

Soon all the valleys were filled with water, the hills disappeared and even the highest mountains sank out of sight. The storm grew fiercer, and the rain fell all through the night without stopping. No land could be seen anywhere — not even the highest mountain top. When the flood reached its peak, Allah commanded: "O earth, swallow up your water; O sky keep back your rain!"(11:14).The rain stopped! The water began to dry up. The clouds began to part to show clear sky, the sunlight dispersed the darkness and, as the level of the water went down, the mountain peaks began to emerge. The Ark was caught by the peak of Mount Judi and rested upon it. This was in a place near the frontiers of modern Turkey, Syria and Iraq.

The Prophet Nuh ﷺ and all the others in the Ark thanked Allah for keeping them safe during the great flood. The Prophet Nuh ﷺ bowed down and prayed: "Praise be to Allah who has saved all the good souls of a sinful nation." Allah rewarded the believers and made the world once again free of wicked people. And He made the Flood and the Ark signs of warning for future generations.

Talk with me

What was the message of the Prophet Nuh ﷺ?

What happened to the sinners?

Say with me

Nuh said: 'Allah will bring it down upon you when He pleases: nor shall you be immune. My counsel will not profit you if Allah seeks to lead you astray, willing though I am to guide you. He is your Lord, and to Him you shall return.'.....Allah's will was revealed to Nuh, saying: 'None of your people will believe in you save those who already believe. Do not grieve at what they do. Build an ark under Our watchful eyes, according to Our bidding. You shall not plead with Me for those who have done wrong: they shall all be drowned.'(11:33-37)

Pray with me

Dear Allah, always guide me to do good deeds and teach me to be responsible for my acts.

16

Faith gives Courage

The Prophet Ibrahim ﷺ (Abraham) was born among people who worshipped the creations of Allah, such as the stars and other heavenly bodies and anything which they could not understand or which had some kind of power like the various forces of nature. Even as a child, the Prophet Ibrahim ﷺ was not satisfied and was interested in knowing the true God. One night, he saw a star and exclaimed: 'This is my Lord.' (6:76) But after a while the star set and it was not visible any more, so the Prophet Ibrahim ﷺ thought that it could not be God. He said: 'I do not love that which fades.' Then he saw moon rising in splendour and said: 'This is my Lord.' But it too went on its course and disappeared. He was sure that it could not be his Lord either. When he saw the rising sun he said: 'This is my Lord.' And when the sun in turn went away, he realized his mistake and said: 'O my people! I am indeed free from your error of giving partners to Allah.' (6:78) 'I will turn my face to Him who has created the heaven and the earth, and live a righteous life...'He was convinced that there was no god but God.

He started questioning the belief of his people and tried to reason with them that what they worshipped were only creations of Allah. The answer he got from them was that these were the gods of their forefathers and they would not leave them. They blindly followed what their elders did, however wrong it was. They refused to see the truth. The Prophet Ibrahim's father was so angry with his message that he turned him out of his house. His people even threw him into a blazing fire, but Allah saved him by making fire become cool. Even this did not convince his people. But nothing could change his true faith in

Allah. He did not even obey Namrud (Nimrod), the ruler of his country. Namrud was also worshipped as a god. He said that, like God, even he could give life or death. The Prophet Ibrahim ﷺ was not scared of him and asked him to make the sun rise from the west, if he was a God. When Namrud had no answer for him, he became angry and forced him to leave the country. The Prophet Ibrahim ﷺ was not scared of anyone, because he feared only Allah. He knew that only Allah was All-Powerful. Faith in Allah is the only thing that can guide and save a believer in this world and in the world to come.

Talk with me

What did the Prophet Ibrahim's people worship?

Why was the Prophet Ibrahim ﷺ not scared of anyone?

Say with me

Tell of Ibrahim, who said to Azar, his father: 'Will you worship idols as your gods? Surely you and all your people are plainly in error.' Thus We show Ibrahim the kingdom of the heavens and the earth, so that he might become a firm believer. (6:74, 75)

Pray with me

Dear Allah, guide me always to see the truth and remove all the fears from my heart. Give me the courage to be on the side of truth, even if my family, friends and others are not with me.

A Wonderful Plan

The Prophet Yusuf ﷺ (Joseph) had a difficult childhood. When he was a young boy, he was thrown by his jealous stepbrothers into a deep, dry well. They wanted to get rid of him, because they did not want to share the love of their father with him. The Prophet Yusuf ﷺ cried for help, but they went away leaving him to die. But Allah had some different plans for him.

The Prophet Yusuf ﷺ had firm faith in Allah and was sure that Allah would help him and therefore was not scared. Allah did not disappoint him. He said "You shall one day tell them the truth of this affair when they will not know you." (12:15)After three days in the well without food or water, he was finally found by traders who were going to Egypt. In Memphis they sold him for 20 dirhams to a nobleman, Aziz. He brought him up like his own son and gave him excellent education and training. The Prophet Yusuf ﷺ turned into a man of remarkable ability and wisdom and later became the chief minister of Egypt.

So the well became the first step for the Prophet Yusuf ﷺ to reach great heights, taken as he was from a small village to the most modern city of that time in Egypt and finally becoming the chief minister. Allah's plans are always best for the believers. What appears as a hardship eventually turns out to be a blessing. We should completely submit our will to Allah.

Talk with me
What happened to the Prophet Yusuf ﷺ when he was a young boy? Was his stepbrothers' plan successful?

Say with me
When Yusuf attained his full manhood, We gave him power and knowledge: thus do We reward those who do right. (12:22)

Pray with me
Thank you, Allah, for taking care of us and making wonderful plans for us.

Patience is Worship

The Prophet Ayyub ﷺ (Job) was a rich and prosperous man. In spite of his prosperity he remained a sincere and a humble follower of Allah. But the unbelievers felt that the Prophet Ayyub ﷺ was such a faithful follower of Allah because of his riches, and if his blessings were taken away, he would not remain as faithful and grateful to Allah.

To show them they were wrong, Allah put him to a test. Within a short period of time, the Prophet Ayyub ﷺ became very poor, his children died and his friends left him. His wife also left him and he became very lonely. Worst of all he became very ill, remaining bedridden for 18 years. But the Prophet Ayyub ﷺ continued to be a devout follower of Allah. He never lost patience or became hopeless or angry. He completely trusted Allah and believed that Allah knew what was best for him. He said: "Truly, distress has seized me, but You are the Most Merciful of those that are merciful." (21:83) Allah said to him:

"Stamp your foot on the ground. Here is water to wash with, it is cool and refreshing. Drink of it too." (38:42) No sooner did the Prophet Ayyub ﷺ take a bath in this water, than his illness was cured and he regained his former health and strength. Allah rewarded him for his patience and belief, in this world and in the Hereafter. Patience in itself is worship which shall be highly rewarded.

Talk with me

Why did the Prophet Ayyub ﷺ suffer?

What pleased Allah?

Say with me

We found him full of patience. He was a good and faithful man. (38:44) Believers, fortify yourself with patience and prayer, Allah is with those who are patient. (2:153)

Pray with me

Dear Allah, bless me with constancy and patience.

The She-Camel

Allah sends His prophets to people who stray from His straight path. One such prophet was Salih, who was sent to the tribe of Thamud. They were believers, but success and development had made them proud. They stopped believing in Allah and His laws. They were cruel to the poor and did not give them the right to use water and common pastures. The Prophet Salih ﷺ was sad to see that what Allah had given to men to use equally, was being controlled by a few powerful men of his tribe.

Once, when there was scarcity of water, the proud, rich people of Thamud did not allow the poor and their cattle to use the springs and common pasture land. This world is a world of trial and Allah puts every man to the test before letting him enter the world of the Hereafter. Allah sent a she-camel as a test for the people of Thamud. The Prophet Salih ﷺ said, "Here is a she-camel: she has same rights of watering as you have, therefore do not harm her lest you be destroyed."(26:155,156) They said, "Are we to follow a mortal who stands alone among us? That would surely be a mistake and madness. Did he alone among us receive this warning? He is indeed a foolish liar!" They did not change their ways and killed the she-camel. They also plotted to kill the Prophet Salih ﷺ.

After three days a terrible earthquake buried the proud, sinful people in their fortress-like houses. It was as if they had never lived there. And Allah saved those who believed and practiced righteousness.

Talk with me

What was the sin of the Thamud?

What happened to the Thamud?

Say with me

"O my people! This she-camel of Allah (*naqat Allah*) is a sign to you: leave her to feed on Allah's free earth, and do her no harm, or you will very soon be punished!' (11:64). And on the night of the third day a mighty earthquake shook the earth, and took them unawares. (7:78) It buried the sinful people in their own homes, which they had made out of stone for security and protection. The morning found them lying flat on their faces in the dust. Nobody could say that it was only the day before that they had dwelt and flourished there. (11:67-68)

Pray with me

Dear Allah, make me share all your gifts equally with everyone, as they also have an equal right to them. Allah, make me a kind and generous person.

The Lessons of Luqman

Luqman was a wise man who lived in Arabia. Allah gave him wisdom and asked him to be thankful to the Almighty. Luqman believed in Allah and asked his son not to worship anyone but Allah and to be regular in prayers. He also asked him to be kind to his parents and not to treat anyone with scorn. Luqman advised him to speak out for justice and forbid evil and to be patient, even in suffering. He told his son: "Allah does not love the arrogant and the boastful, but the humble. One should not even walk proudly on the earth and should be polite and speak softly."

He added that Allah's laws are for man's own good. True wisdom is divine wisdom. They cannot be separated. Wise are those who truly believe in Allah and His laws and live according to His will. In this way they also live in accordance with their own nature as made by Allah. Luqman believed that human beings in all their thoughts and actions should be moderate like other creations of Allah.

Talk with me

What was Luqman's advice to his son?
How is true wisdom divine wisdom?

Say with me

Whoever submits his whole self to Allah and is a doer of good, has grasped indeed the firmest hand-hold: and to Allah shall all things return. (31:22)

Pray with me

Thank you, Allah, for guiding us towards the path of true wisdom.

Zamzam

The Prophet Ibrahim ﷺ had complete faith in Allah and he was always ready to fulfill His every command. He spread the message of Allah first in Iraq, his own country, and later in Syria, Palestine and Egypt. Allah ordered him to go with his wife Hajar (Hagar) and their newborn son, Ismail (Ishmael) to a place which later came to be known as Makkah. This spot was located in an arid desert. The Arabian Peninsula was an unfriendly and lonely place with few inhabitants.

They reached there after a very hard journey. When the Prophet Ibrahim ﷺ started to go away, leaving his wife and little Ismail, fearfully Hajar asked, "Why are you leaving us alone here? Are you leaving us here to die?" He replied, "Allah has commanded me to do this." Then Hajar was no longer afraid, she replied: "If Allah has ordered you to do so, then He will not let us die."

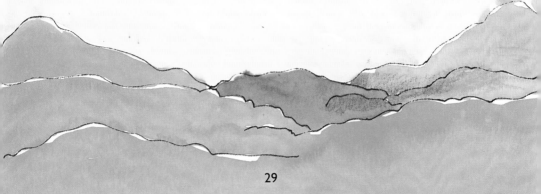

After some time, little Ismail started crying for water. There was not a single drop of water to be found. There was neither a well nor a spring anywhere in sight. She became scared, but knew that Allah would surely help her. She ran between the hills of Safa and Marwa, hoping to find water for her son. She did not give up. To her surprise, she saw a spring gushing out from beneath the little foot of Ismail. Allah had made a spring flow where there had been none just a while ago. This spring later came to be known as Zamzam. Gradually this spring attracted people and later a small town grew up and was called Makkah. Allah's commands are always a part of a larger divine scheme.

In His divine scheme there is always a sound reason behind every event, which takes place on the earth and in the heavens. Here it was to create people with strong character. Later it was in Makkah that Prophet Muhammad ﷺ and most of his companions were born. Allah always takes care of His believers who never leave His path.

Allah was very happy with Hajar's patient perseverance in faith. Allah made it compulsory for all those who go on the Hajj to repeat Hajar's act of running between the two mountains, so that pilgrims may walk in her footsteps. Muslims should not forget her great faith and patience and should try themselves to have these qualities.

Talk with me

What happened to Hajar and little Ismail in Makkah?
Why was Allah happy with Hajar?

Say with me

Behold! Safa and Marwa are among the symbols of Allah. So those who come on a pilgrimage should run between them. (2:158)

Pray with me

Dear Allah, please strengthen my faith and help me never to become discouraged by hardships.

Prayers

Allah answers the prayers of those who completely believe in Him and expect blessings only from Him. The Prophet Zakariya ﷿ (Zacharias) was a worried man because his people were not good followers of Allah. Therefore, he wanted a son who would continue the work of Allah sincerely. The Prophet Zakariya ﷿ prayed: "Allah, grant me of Your own Grace upright descendants. You hear all prayers!"(3:38) The angels came and said: "God bids you to rejoice in the birth of Yahya (John the Baptist). He shall be noble and chaste, a

prophet and a righteous man." (3:39) He wondered, "Allah, how shall I have a son when I am so old and my wife is barren?" (3:40) But Allah said: "So it shall be. It is easy for Me, for I created you, before which you were nothing."(19:10) When the Prophet Zakariya ﷺ asked for a sign, Allah said, "Your sign is that for three days and nights you shall not be able to speak, though otherwise healthy."(19:10)

The Prophet Yahya ﷺ was kind to his parents and he grew up as a humble, gentle and straight forward person. He was a preacher of truth and led a life of solitude. His main mission was to pave the way for the Prophet Isa ﷺ (Jesus), to renew the message of Allah, which had been corrupted and lost among the Israelites.

Talk with me
Why did the Prophet Zakariya ﷺ want a son?
What was the mission of the Prophet Yahya ﷺ ?

Say with me
'Rejoice, Zakariya,' came the answer. 'You shall be given a son, and he shall be called Yahya; a name no man has borne before him.'(19:8)

Pray with me
Dear Allah, You are so compassionate and so merciful and answer all our prayers. Thank you, Allah, for listening to us and taking care of all our needs.

Miracles

The Prophet Isa ﷺ (Jesus) was blessed with the power of miracles. He used miracles to convince people about the truth of his mission. He started spreading the message of Allah as a child in the arms of his mother, Maryam (Mary). At an age when no child can even speak, he defended Maryam when she was blamed for a sin. He cured the blind and the lepers and brought many people back to life. The Prophet Isa ﷺ would even breathe life into birds made of clay with Allah's blessing.

Still he struggled to spread his message, only a few answered his call. Even his disciples from time to time kept asking for more miracles to confirm their faith in Allah. In fact, these requests showed a lack of faith.

One day, the Prophet Isa ﷺ was sitting with his disciples, at the time for dinner. They had no food and they said to him: "Isa, son of Maryam, can your Allah send down to us from heaven a table spread with food?" He did not like their doubts. "Have fear of Allah," he admonished them, "If you are true believers." They replied: "We want to eat from it, so that we may reassure our hearts and know that what you said to us is true, and that we may be witnesses to it."

"Allah", said the Prophet Isa ﷺ, "send down to us from heaven a table spread with food, that it may mark a feast for the first of us and the last of us: a sign from You. Give us our sustenance; You are the best Provider." "I am sending one to you," replied Allah, "but if any one of you disbelieves after this, he shall be punished as no man will ever be punished." (5:110-115)

Talk with me
What was so special about the Prophet Isa ﷺ?
What did the Prophet Isa's disciples ask for?

Say with me
Isa is like Adam in the sight of Allah. He created him from dust and then said to him: "Be," and he was.(3:59)

Pray with me
Dear Allah, save me from all kind of doubts. Increase my faith in You and Your guidance.

The Companions of the Cave

Allah's promise of goodness and mercy to those who have complete faith in Him and who serve Him truly is exemplified in the story of the companions of the cave. In 250 A.D. seven young men of the city of Ephesus (near the western coast of Turkey) accepted the teachings of the Prophet Isa ﷺ. But at that time King Daqyanus (Decius), the ruler of Roman Empire, was an unbeliever and he killed those who believed in the message of the Prophet Isa ﷺ, to worship Allah. Very courageously these men continued to preach the message of the one and only God. When the king's soldiers were about to capture them, they were guided by Allah to take refuge in a dark cave in the mountains outside the town. Once in the safety of the cave, they prayed, "Lord, have mercy on us and guide us through our ordeal." (18:10)

Allah made them sleep in the cave for many years. All the while their faithful dog too lay in slumber with its legs stretched across the entrance of the cave, in the same pose he might have assumed when guarding them from harm. Allah is All-Powerful. Even time works in accordance with His will. The world around them changed as about 300 years passed, but they stayed the same, as Allah desired them to. The cruel king Daqyanus had died, and most of his empire had by now accepted the message of the Prophet Isa ﷺ and believed in one God. The present king, Theodosius II, was also a believer. Life changes, nothing remains the same forever.

When the appointed hour came, they rose from their sleep. They looked around, feeling a little lost, and began questioning each other in astonishment. "How long have you been here?" asked one. "A day, or maybe just a few hours." replied another. "Your Lord knows best how long you have stayed here," said the third. "Let one of you go to the city with this silver coin and bring back any wholesome food he finds there. But be cautious, and don't tell anybody about this cave or us. If they capture you, they will stone you to death, or make you renounce your faith." The young men did not know that they had passed more than 300 years in the cave in deep sleep and the world had completely changed.

But when the young man gave the coin to the shopkeeper, he stared at him in amazement: the coin was ancient and no longer in use. He

thought that the young man must have found a hidden
treasure. The news of a young man with an ancient coin spread
like wildfire in the market, then all over town, and
finally reached the king. The young man realized that

centuries must have passed since the time he and his companions escaped from this town. The people thought it a miracle that Allah had saved them in such a strange way. They would not let him go till he led them to the cave and his companions. The king, too, arrived to seek their blessings. When the young men died, a shrine was built at the cave as a memorial to them.

Allah can change the situation before we are aware, and our hope in Him is not futile, and even when we are on the brink of despair, a change is surely working in the world before the world itself realizes it.

Talk with me
Why did the young men hide in the cave?
How did Allah protect the young men?

Say with me
When you turn away from them and the things they worship other than Allah, go to the cave for shelter: your Lord will shower His mercies on you and prepare for you a means of safety. (18:16)

Pray with me
Dear Allah, protect me from evil and give me the courage to stand up for truth in the face of all difficulties.

The Proud People Ad

The Ad were great builders. They made beautiful buildings and many canals so that their country was covered with fields and gardens. There was no other city like the many-columned city of Iram. The Ad, very skilled in the arts, and sciences and were a cultured people. In the beginning they followed the religion of the Prophet Nuh ﷺ and worshipped only Allah. But with the passage of time, they started thinking that all that they had was due to their own achievements. They forgot that they were His creatures and whatever skills and wisdom they possessed had all been given by Allah. Like any other people who prize material things, they became proud and obstinate and fell into evil ways. Every community (also each person) is given a period of time, when they have the chance to give up their proud ways, seek forgiveness and turn back to Allah. He forgives those who change their ways and opens the gates of Paradise for them. To give the Ad people the opportunity to get rid of the sins of pride and arrogance and to come back on to the straight path, Allah sent the Prophet Hud ﷺ to warn them of what would happen to them if they did not repent.

The Prophet Hud ﷺ asked them to give up pride, worship Allah and obey His laws. "You build strong fortresses, hoping that you may last for ever. When you exercise your power on the weak, you act like cruel tyrants. Fear Allah and follow me." But they ridiculed him and called him a fool and a liar. As a result, there was a drought and they suffered three long years of famine. But they still did not change. Then there was a violent storm. It went on for seven nights and eight days and completely destroyed them. Allah, in His mercy, saved the Prophet Hud ﷺ and his followers.

Talk with me
What sin did the Ad commit?
What happened to the Ad?

Say with me

"'Who is superior to us in strength?' Did they not see that Allah, who created them, was superior to them in strength?"(41:15)

Pray with me

Dear Allah, save me from pride and cruelty to the weak, and do not let me break Your laws.

The Building of The Kabah

The Prophet Ibrahim ﷺ with his wife Hajar and their son Ismail settled in a lonely desert in Arabia, as desired by Allah. After the appearance of the spring of ZamZam, more people began to settle there. Soon it developed into a small city, which later came to be known as Makkah.

Allah ordered the Prophets Ibrahim ﷺ and Ismail ﷺ to build the House of God – the Kabah at a particular place in Makkah. They immediately started to work and brought stones and boulders from the nearby hill. They prayed, "Our Lord, accept this from us. You are the All-hearing, the All-seeing. Our Lord, make us bow to You, and make our offspring a nation which bows to You and show us our ways of worship." (2:127,128) They prayed to Allah throughout the making of the Kabah. Allah helped them in their efforts, giving them the strength and perseverance to face the hardships of this tremendous task. They prayed for a prophet to be born in their family, a prophet who would teach them wisdom and purify their faith. Their prayers were answered when the Prophet Muhammad ﷺ was born to their descendants.

After the House of the God was ready, they cleaned it. Allah asked the Prophet Ibrahim ﷺ to call the people to perform Hajj. It is the duty of every Muslim to go on Hajj once in a lifetime, provided their means and their health permits. Hajj was made one of the five pillars of Islam, to be performed in the spirit of brotherhood. The pilgrimage is the symbol of Allah being the focal point in the lives of Muslims.

Talk with me
What did Allah order the Prophet Ibrahim ﷺ to do?
What prayers did the Prophets Ibrahim ﷺ and Ismail ﷺ say?

Say with me
The House of God is full of blessings and guidance for all the worlds. (3:96)

Pray with me
Dear Allah, we are very grateful to you for the Kabah, where all of us from different parts of the world can come together and pray for Your blessings and guidance.

Actions Make You What You are

Everyone is responsible and accountable for his or her deeds. One cannot escape one's acts before Allah. He knows all and, accordingly, one is rewarded or punished.

Queen Asiya, wife of Firawn (Pharaoh) is one of the most respected ladies in Islam. Firawn had ordered that all the boys born to the

Children of Israel should be killed. The Prophet Musa's (Moses) mother to save her infant kept him in a basket and put it into the water. He was found by Queen Asiya who was a loving and a kind-hearted person. When her husband wanted to kill the infant Musa, she begged him not to, saying, "This child may bring joy to both of us. He may show promise and we may adopt him as our son."(28:9) Finally, Firawn agreed and the Prophet Musa ﷺ was brought up in the palace under the loving care of Queen Asiya. When everyone in Egypt worshipped Firawn, his own wife believed in Allah and in His supreme power. She knew that, like everything else, even Firawn was the creation of Allah. It is very difficult to believe in truth when everyone around you believes in lies and also when you suffer because of your beliefs. Her faith in Allah gave her this strength. She did not care for worldly pleasures. She cared only for Allah's reward in the Hereafter. She prayed to Allah to save her from Firawn and his sins and grant her a place in paradise.

In complete contrast to her are the unbelieving wives of the Prophets Nuh ﷺ and Lut ﷺ (Lot). They believed neither in Allah nor in the message of the prophets. They were wicked. No one becomes righteous by being related to the righteous. One has to believe in Allah and live according to His will and laws. Their husbands could in no way protect them from Allah's punishment — which they deserved. The same was true of the Prophet Nuh's unbelieving son, Kanan and the Prophet Ibrahim's unbelieving father, Azar.

One soul cannot take the merits of another any more than a pure soul can be injured by its nearness to a bad soul. Each person is responsible before Allah. It is deeds which makes a person good or bad, not the circumstances of birth or family. One is a Muslim because of his deeds and not just because of his birth. One cannot lay the blame for one's acts on others or on circumstances. One is responsible for them oneself.

Talk with me

Why is Queen Asiya honoured in Islam?
What do you understand by this story?

Say with me

Allah has set an example to the unbelievers in the wife of Nuh and the wife of Lut. They were married to two of Our righteous servants and deceived them. Their husbands could in no way protect them from Allah. They were told: 'Enter the fire, together with those that shall enter it.' But to the faithful, Allah has set an example in Pharaoh's wife, who said: 'Lord, build me a house with You in Paradise and deliver me from Pharaoh and his misdeeds. Deliver me from the wicked nation.' (66:10-11)

Pray with me

Dear Allah, always guide me to the life of righteousness and bless me with Your wisdom so that I always do good. Help me always to act as desired by You, and earn my place in Paradise.

Dreams

Due to the evil plan of Zulaykha, the wife of Aziz, the Prophet Yusuf ﷺ was disgraced and sent to prison. But Allah had his own plans. The wicked might plot but, in the end, everything is used by Allah in the Universal Plan for its own good purpose. Going to prison opened another chapter in the Prophet Yusuf's life. There were two men in the prison who were earlier royal servants. One day they asked the Prophet Yusuf ﷺ to tell them the meaning of their strange dreams. One of them said, "I see myself in a dream pressing wine." (12:36) The other said, "I see myself carrying bread on my head, and birds are pecking at it."(12:36) The Prophet Yusuf ﷺ explained, "One of you will pour wine for his king to drink; as for the other, he will hang and the birds will peck at his head."

One day some years later the King of Egypt had an unusual dream. He saw seven fat cows being eaten by seven thin ones, and seven green ears of corn turning into seven dry ones. The King's advisers were unable to understand the meaning of this dream. It was then that the royal servant who was still alive remembered the Prophet Yusuf ﷺ and came to him. The Prophet Yusuf ﷺ explained that in the next seven years Egypt would experience great prosperity, but that they would be followed by seven years of terrible drought and famine. He also advised that in the first seven years whatever crops were grown should mostly be saved. The king was very pleased and made him the minister of granaries. The Prophet Yusuf's wisdom helped not only Egypt but also the neighbouring countries during the famine.

Talk with me

What were the dreams of the royal servants?

What was the meaning of the King's dream?

Say with me

Thus did We establish Yusuf in the land, and he dwelt there as he pleased. We bestow Our mercy on whom We will, and shall never deny the righteous their reward. Better is the reward of the Hereafter for those who believe in Allah and keep from evil. (12:57)

Pray with me

Dear Allah, help me to use my resources and intelligence for the well-being of mankind.

Never Cheat

The Prophet Ibrahim  had many descendants, who spread far and wide all over the Arabian Peninsula and the present-day Middle East, forming various tribes and nations. One of them was a tribe known as the people of Madyan. They lived on the Arabian coast of the Red Sea. This was the territory through which most of the trading caravans passed. The ships would also unload their goods in the harbours along the coast.

The power money gave them corrupted them and took them away from the path of Allah. They started doing wrong things in business and religion. They stopped believing in Allah and the Hereafter. They were traders and did business through wrong and unfair means. They gave short measures and weights and did not give people what was rightfully due to them. They cheated people with all sorts of tricks to increase their profits. They also robbed travelling merchants passing through the highway. Even the pilgrims travelling to the House of Allah in Makkah were not spared.

Allah sent the Prophet Shuayb ﷺ to give them another chance to repent and turn back to Him. He called on to them to return to worship Allah and adopt truthful ways in their dealings with others.   He advised them again and again, "Give just measure and weight, and do not withhold from the people the things that are their due. Do no mischief on the earth after it has been set in order: that will be best for you, if you have Faith." (7:85) The Prophet Shuayb ﷺ reminded them of Allah's favours and also of the future of sinners like them. He asked them to give up wrong ways of doing business, because this would cut short their prosperity both in this world and in the Hereafter. He asked them to earn according to Allah's laws and take only what they rightfully deserved. He told them that if they did as he said, they would be satisfied and happy like him.

But the people did not listen to him and warned him: "O Shuayb! We shall certainly drive you out of our city and those who believe in you unless you follow our ways." (7:88) "Were it not for your family, we should certainly have stoned you! For you do not hold any great position amongst us!" (11:91) They rather advised him to return to the old ways of oppressing the poor and the weak and being cruel to them. The dishonest and wicked people of Madyan were destroyed by an earthquake. The Prophet Shuayb ﷺ and his followers were saved, as they had already left the Madyan for Makkah.

Talk with me
Who were people of Madyan?
Why were the people of Madyan punished by Allah?

Say with me
Woe to the unjust who, when others measure for them, demand the full amount, but when they measure or weigh for others, defraud them! (83:1)

Pray with me
Dear Allah, make me a just and a fair person. Guide me to earn my living according to Your laws and not through any kind of cheating or wrong means.

Greed

At the time when the Prophet Musa ﷺ (Moses) was fighting against the sins of Firawn and for the rights of Children of Israel, there lived a rich man, Qarun (Korah), belonging to the same tribe, who was a friend of Firawn (Pharaoh). He was friendly with the king for his own personal gains, and did not care for the sufferings of his people. He was a miser. He did not use his money for any good deeds or for the good of the poor. The money was for his selfish pleasure.

The righteous among his people would tell him: "Seek the Abode of the Hereafter with the help of the wealth, which Allah has bestowed upon you. Do not forget that portion of the wealth, which is to be spent in this world: do good to others the way Allah does good to you. Do not look out for opportunities to cause mischief on the earth, for Allah does not love those who do mischief." (28:77)

Qarun did not hear the warning hidden in these words and would proudly reply: "These treasures have been given to me because of my special knowledge and skills." (28:78) He arrogantly believed that whatever he had was nothing other than the fruit of his own efforts and was naturally due to him because of his cleverness. Some people even admired his wealth and the position it gave him in society. They thought the way he thought also—that it is the glitter and riches of this world that really count. They envied him, saying: "Oh, if only we had those things which Qarun has. He is indeed a lucky man!" (28:79) Those who had real knowledge and were wise were not at all impressed by Qarun's possessions and standing. They knew that the things of the world pass. They are of no use in themselves unless they are put to good use. It has been repeated time and again by the prophets that the treasures of the earth are not given to man as a reward for something. They are given to him to test him in this world and find out if he obeys the commands of Allah if he looks after his treasures without being miserly, shares them with his fellow human beings and gives alms out of them to the needy. Only if the wealth entrusted to one on earth is used in a God-fearing and rightful manner, does it serve its purpose of giving its owner the everlasting riches of Paradise. Qarun was not of the wise. He was not of the God-fearing men. He was unmindful of the Day of Judgement and the Hereafter. He had forgotten that Allah had destroyed whole generations before him, whose wealth and strength were even greater than his. (28:78) They might have enjoyed their wealth in this life for quite a long

time, using it in a miserly and arrogant way on themselves, but they would certainly be called to account for this behaviour later on.

And this was what happened in Qarun's case too. All of a sudden, when his appointed time had run out, Allah made the earth swallow him and his house. His wealth and power could not save him. Those who had envied his position only the day before began to say: "Ah! Allah gives much to some and very little to other, just as it pleases Him. If He so wished, He might have made the earth swallow us too! But He was gracious to us. Ah! One thing is sure: never will those who reject Allah prosper." (28:82)

Talk with me
What did wise men think of Qarun's wealth?
What happened to Qarun?

Say with me
The wicked are not called immediately to account for their sins. (28:78)

Pray with me
Dear Allah, guide me to use my wealth given by You for the poor and the greater good of mankind. Allah, bless me with the riches of Paradise.

Another Chance

Nineveh (near Baghdad) was one of the famous cities of ancient times. Its people were rich, powerful and wicked. Earlier they had been believers in Allah. Allah asked the Prophet Yunus ﷺ (Jonah) to go to the city and guide its people to the right path. He preached faith in Allah and in His unity and asked them to be righteous. But they did not listen to him rather made fun of him. He became disappointed and angry and left the city, warning that Allah would punish them. The task given to him by Allah seemed much too difficult and it discouraged him, so he ran away from it.

He boarded a ship, but it was soon struck by a violent storm. The sailors, being unbelievers, were superstitious and thought that the Prophet Yunus ﷺ had brought them ill-luck. So they threw him into the sea where he was swallowed by a fish. In the dark, damp insides of the fish, he realised his mistake in passing judgement on the people and in becoming hopeless and giving up his work. He cried, "There is no god but You. Glory be to You! I have done wrong." (21:87) Allah heard his prayers and gave him another chance to fulfill his mission. The fish, at the command of Allah, brought him to the beach. This time he was successful in his mission. The people believed him and repented for their sins, getting a new base of life for themselves and their city. Following Allah's commandments and submitting to His will, brings happiness and inner peace in this world and great rewards in the Hereafter.

Talk with me

Why did the Prophet Yunus ﷺ leave his people?
What did he realise inside the fish?

Say with me

"We answered his (Yunus) prayer and delivered him from distress. Thus shall We save the true believers." (21:88) Wait, then, the judgement of your Lord and do not act like him (Yunus) who was swallowed by the whale when he called out in despair. Had his Lord not bestowed on him His Grace, he would have been abandoned in the open to be blamed by all. But his Lord chose him for His own and made of him a righteous man. (68:48)

Pray with me

Dear Allah, give me patience, intelligence and courage to do the work I am born for. Do not let me judge others, as You know better.

Two Gardens

Once there lived two friends, Tamilkha who was rich and Mutis who was very poor. The rich one owned two beautiful, well-watered gardens full of flowers and fruit-bearing trees. Swelling with pride, Tamilkha would say, while talking to Mutis and showing him his gardens: "I am richer than you and my people are mightier than yours." Tamilkha loved his garden and its good things, but never thought that these were the bounties of the Lord gifted to him just for some time. He was completely engrossed in his gardens and depended on them. He did not realise that this was a temporary world which was not going to last. Only in Allah there is truth and hope.

"Surely this will never perish!" he would say to himself, whenever he entered the gardens. "Nor do I believe that the Hour of Doom will

ever come. Even if I return to my Lord, I should surely find a better place than this." (18:36-37) "Better" for him meant "where there was more wealth and power".

Mutis, hearing his words and seeing him behaving with arrogance, asked him once, "Have you no faith in Him who created you from dust, from a little germ, and made you into a man? As for myself, Allah is my Lord. I will associate none with Him. When you entered your garden, why did you not say: 'What Allah has ordained must surely come to pass: there is no strength except in Allah?'"

Mutis completely believed in Allah and was grateful to Him for everything he had. He said, "Wealth and children are the ornaments

of this life. But deeds of lasting merit are better rewarded by our Lord." (18:46)

The very next day calamity struck. Tamilkha's gardens were laid waste. His fruits were destroyed and the vines tumbled down upon their trellises. He walked around the ruined gardens in grief, for he could see that everything he had laboured and depended on was gone. But he had nobody but himself to blame for what had happened.

"How I wish I had served no other gods besides my Lord!" cried Tamilkha, his heart filled with remorse. It was too late to save the gardens, but it was not too late to save his soul.

Talk with me
What was the difference in the thinking of Tamilkha and Mutis?
Why were Tamilkha's gardens destroyed?

Say with me
Ultimately, it is to Allah that one must turn for help for in such ordeals. Protection comes only from Allah, His is the best recompense, and His the best requital. (18:45)

Pray with me
Dear Allah, guide me to depend only on You. Thank You for always being there for me.

The Magicians

During the time of Firawn, the citizens of Egypt were forced to practice the pagan religion and magic. Firawn was the supreme god. The Egyptians were also very cruel to the Children of Israel. Allah asked the Prophet Musa ﷺ to preach to them the oneness of Allah and the glory of righteousness. Allah also enabled him to perform miracles to show the people the falsity of the religion based on magic and cheap tricks which they practiced.

The Prophet Musa ﷺ, accompanied by the Prophet Harun ﷺ (Aaron) went to Firawn's court. He said to Firawn: "O Firawn! I am a messenger from the Lord of the Worlds. Now I have come to you with a clear Sign from your Lord: so let the Children of Israel depart along with me." (7:104-105) Firawn became furious and asked: "Who is your Lord, Musa?" To this Prophet Musa ﷺ replied: "Our Lord is He Who gave all creatures their special forms, and then rightly guided them."
Firawn did not believe his words and challenged him to show the sign. "The Prophet Musa ﷺ threw down his rod, and behold! It was a serpent, and all could see it plainly. And he drew out his hand, and behold! It was white to all beholders!" (7:107-108) Allah's Clear Signs did not convince Firawn and his ministers. They refused even to think that the Prophet Musa's message might be true and they said: "This is nothing but sorcery!" (26:34)

They thought they could defeat the Prophet Musa ﷺ with the help of their own magicians. All the sorcerers of the land were called to the court on the festival day and Firawn promised a suitable reward to any one of them who could with his tricks defeat the Prophet Musa ﷺ. They challenged the Prophet Musa ﷺ. They threw down their rods and suddenly they changed into snakes crawling and hissing on the ground in front of them. The people, impressed by their magic, drew back in fear. But Allah was with the Prophet Musa ﷺ and advised him to throw down his rod. "And behold! it turned into a snake and swallowed all the falsehoods." (7:117)

The magicians could see that this was not a trick but a real sign of Allah. They were touched by the glorious light of Allah. They immediately bowed down and said that they believed in Allah, the Lord of the Worlds, the Lord of Musa and Harun.(7:120-121) They asked for Allah's forgiveness for their sins and for their practice of magic which had been forced on them. This made Firawn mad with anger. To save his authority in front of his subjects he accused the magicians of being the secret followers of the Prophets

Musa ﷺ and Harun ﷺ. He warned them of severe punishment and even death. But they were scared not of the punishment of Firawn but of Allah. They were ready to suffer and die. (7:126) Their only desire was to be forgiven by Allah. (20:73) The light of the message of Allah made them strong and fearless of the worldly power of Firawn. The truth is most powerful and it gives strength to those who believe in it. Allah is merciful and forgiving. He can enlighten anyone—even the sinners—and teach them to follow the straight path.

Talk with me

What did Allah ask the Prophet Musa ﷺ to do?
How did Firawn's magicians become believers?

Say with me

He who comes to his Lord as a sinner (on Judgement Day), - shall be cast into hell: there in shall he neither die nor live. But such as come to Him as believers who have done righteous deeds shall be exalted to the highest rank. (20:74, 75)

Pray with me

Thank you, Allah, for guiding me to the right path and, please, never let me wander away from it. Bless me with the strength of the true faith.

The Escape

The Prophet Musa ﷺ continued to teach his message to the Egyptians: to come to the right path, worship Allah, stop their cruelties and allow the Children of Israel to leave Egypt. They did not listen and were punished by Allah. They were struck by famines, floods and diseases. After every punishment, they begged the Prophet Musa ﷺ to save them. But as soon as they were saved, they went back to their old, cruel, evil ways. The cruelties of Firawn and the Egyptians kept on increasing. There was a reign of terror with no mercy shown to the Israelites.

Then Allah asked the Prophet Musa ﷺ to take the Children of Israel out of Egypt, saying: "Travel by night with my servants; for surely you shall be pursued."(26:52) On an appointed night they set out on their journey. It was 430 years earlier that the Prophet Yusuf ﷺ had brought them to Egypt. They went through the wilderness towards the Red Sea so that their enemies would not spot them. When Firawn came to know of their departure, he called out his army and at sunrise they set out after them. The Israelites could not move fast because of the women and children and all the belongings they were carrying. Soon Firawn's army came quite close. When they found themselves trapped between the Red Sea and the Egyptian army, they were terrified: "We are sure to be overtaken." (26:61) But the Prophet Musa ﷺ set their fears at rest: "By no means! My Lord is with me! Soon will He guide me!" (26:62) Allah then inspired the Prophet Musa ﷺ: "Strike the sea with your rod." (26:63) As soon as his rod touched the sea, "it divided, and each separate part became like the huge, firm mass of a mountain." (26:63)

The Children of Israel were amazed; the sandy bottom of the sea was laid bare and dry in front of them. A safe path across the seabed had opened up. The frightening waves were held up high in the air on both sides of the passage. With their hearts in their mouths, looking back at the speedily approaching forces, the Israelites ran fast and reached the other bank. Then the power keeping the walls of water up in the air let them loose and the sea collapsed on Firawn and his men. In the blink of an eye, it had swallowed them up one and all.

Firawn, who considered himself not only the mightiest ruler on earth, but even a god, was destroyed in just a matter of a few seconds. Thus Allah delivered the Prophet Musa ﷺ and all who were with him, and drowned all the others. (26:65-66) In the last moments of his life, Firawn realized that the Prophet Musa's message was correct and that indeed Allah was the only God and was All-Powerful. He cried out to Allah: "Now I believe that no god exists except Allah in whom the Children of Israel believe. To Him I give up myself." But Allah rejected his prayer: "Only now! But before this you were a rebel and a wrongdoer." (10:90, 91) After he was drowned, his body was taken out of the sea and according to the old Egyptian custom, was mummified-an example for future generations.

Talk with me
How did the Children of Israel escape from Egypt?
What happened to Firawn and his army?

Say with me
We delivered Musa and all who were with him; but we drowned the others. In this is a sign: but most of them do not believe. (26:65-67)

Pray with me
Dear Allah, guide me away from pride and cruelty. Make me tolerant towards all kinds of people.

Faith Triumphs

The Children of Israel were in great trouble because of being attacked and defeated by the Philistines, Amalekites, Amorites and other tribes around the eleventh century B.C. These defeats were, in fact, a lesson to bring them back to the path of Allah. King Talut (Saul) moved with a large force to fight against the enemy, but his forces were indisciplined and did not have complete faith in Allah. They were scared of Jalut (Goliath), a giant Philistine, who was the commander of the enemy army and the greatest warrior of that time.

There was just a small group who had perfect confidence in Allah and in the cause for which they were fighting. Among them was Dawud (David) who was a young shepherd boy. Everyone used to make fun of him. But his faith in Allah made him more than a match for them. He did not have any arms or armour, except for his shepherds sling and his immense faith in Allah. He picked up five smooth pebbles on the spot from the stream, and used his sling to destroy Jalut. The numbers do not count, but faith, determination and the blessing of Allah are important. Pure faith in Allah brings His reward in many forms. In the case of Dawud, it was instant recognition, power, wisdom and other gifts.

Dawud became very popular and was made the king. Allah gave gifts to Dawud in plenty. He became a wise and a just king. He was taught the art of melting iron and the skill to make armour, for the defence of righteousness. He was also blessed by the gifts of poetry and music. His voice was so melodious that when he sang the praises of Allah, at daybreak and at dusk, the hills and the whole of creation sang aloud with him. He could understand the language of the birds. Allah chose him to be His prophet at the age of forty and gave him a Book of

Revelation called Zabur, or the Psalms.

The fame of the Prophet Dawud's sound and fair judgement spread far and wide, and people would throng his court to have him decide their cases. He was blessed with great wisdom, so that he could judge between the truth and falsehood.

Talk with me

How could a simple shepherd boy like Dawud kill a great warrior like Jalut?
What were the gifts with which the Prophet Dawud ﷺ was blessed by Allah?

Say with me

When they advanced to meet Jalut and his forces, they prayed: 'Our Lord, fill our hearts with steadfastness and make our steps firm: help us against those that reject faith.' By Allah's will they routed them; and Dawud killed Jalut; and Allah gave him power and wisdom and taught him whatever He willed. (2:251)

Pray with me

Dear Allah, bless me with deep faith in You, so that I never become scared of evil, however strong it might be, and I am able to destroy it with Your blessing.

Allah is All-Powerful

The Prophet Uzayr ﷺ was a pious man who lived in the fifth century B.C. He had great faith in Allah and His power over life and death. One day, when he was travelling as usual on his donkey, he happened to notice a ruined city. Looking at the ruins which had no sign of human occupation, he felt sadness in his heart and said to himself:

"Oh! How shall Allah ever bring it to life, after it seems so dead?" (2:259) Allah is All-Hearing and All-Knowing. There and then He brought death to the Prophet Uzayr ﷺ and his donkey. One hundred

years passed and Allah brought him back to life and asked: "What do you think, how long did you stay like this?" The Prophet Uzayr عليه السلام replied, "Maybe a day or a part of it." Allah said, "No, you have remained in this state for a hundred years." The Prophet Uzayr عليه السلام was surprised to see his food and drink which was still fresh. Allah continued, "Now look at your donkey: there is nothing left of it but its bones. Watch what We do: how We bring together its scattered bones right there in front of your eyes and cloth them with the flesh, then cover the flesh with hide and restore your donkey to you. This is a sign for you to see. And for people to see it too, and believe." The Prophet Uzayr عليه السلام was struck dumb and exclaimed, "I know indeed that Allah has power over all things!" (2:259) There is no power greater than that of Allah, who is the Lord of life and death. Time is nothing to Him, though it affects different things in different ways.

Some things never change, some wait to be raised to life while yet others fall apart. But Allah can restore any of them to their original form at any time. He has everything under His control. Therefore, the believers must never forget that there is life after death and reaffirm their belief in the Hereafter.

Talk with me

What did Allah do to the Prophet Uzayr ﷺ?
What lesson do we learn from this story?

Say with me

He asks: 'Who will give life to rotten bones?' Say: 'He who first brought them into being will give them life again: He who gives you from the green tree a fire to light your fuel with.' Has He who created the heavens and the earth no power to create their like? That He surely has. He is the All-Knowing Creator. When He decrees a thing, He need only say: 'Be,' and it is. Glory be to Him who has control of all things. To Him you shall all be recalled. (36:77-83)

Pray with me

Dear Allah, You are All-Powerful and everything is in Your control. Help me always to remember this.

The Web and the Nest

When the Prophet Muhammad's message was spreading far and wide and his followers were growing in numbers, the Quraysh and other unbelievers in Makkah decided to kill the Prophet to stop the spread of his message. One evening, the Prophet was told by the Angel Jibril (Gabriel) not to sleep in his bed because his enemies were plotting to kill him. So Ali lay down on the Prophet's bed under his blanket, so that the enemies would not realise that the Prophet had left Makkah. The Prophet Muhammad ﷺ decided to leave quietly in the night with

Abu Bakr. But instead of going directly to Madinah, they hid themselves in the Cave of Thawr, three miles out of Makkah. On their third day, they heard a Makkan search party at the entrance of the cave. Abu Bakr was scared, but the Prophet assured him: "Do not despair, Allah is with us." (9:40).When the Makkans went away, the Prophet and Abu Bakr looked out and were surprised to see a freshly spun spider's web across the entrance and a newly made pigeon's nest at the side. That was why no one had even looked inside.

One day later they resumed their journey to Madinah. They took a longer route and travelled only during the night for seven days. When they reached Madinah, they were welcomed by a joyous crowd. The Prophet Muhammad ﷺ and his followers stayed with the people of the city and continued to spread the message of Islam with their help.

Talk with me
Why did the Prophet Muhammad ﷺ leave Makkah?
What happened when the Makkan search party reached the cave?

Say with me
They schemed – but Allah also schemed. Allah is most profound in the way He works! (8:30)

Pray with me
Thank you, Allah, for always being with us and saving us from evil.

Sabbath Breakers

The Sabbath was instituted by the law of the Prophet Musa ﷺ.
Saturday was made the day of the Sabbath. On the Sabbath, the
Children of Israel had just to worship Allah and not work at all.

This is a story of the people who lived in the ancient town of Aila (the
modern Aqaba) which was near the sea. Fishing, like any other activity,
was banned on the Sabbath day. Due to this practice the fish used to
come up openly on the day of the Sabbath, but not on other days when
fishing was allowed. This was a great temptation to those who were

not of firm faith and who believed more in having all the good things of life. These greedy men would dig ditches so that the fish could come and be trapped in them. The next day they would collect the fish. In this way, it appeared that they had not broken the law but, in reality, they had broken the law of Allah. Those who did not observe the law in spirit and used tricks to escape the ban were turned into hateful apes.

To be a true believer, one has not just to practice the discipline of a religion but has also to believe in its spirit. Then one would not try to find ways to escape the laws of Allah and at the same time pretend to be believers. Allah knows all and nothing can be hidden from Him.

Talk with me

What was the Sabbath and how did the Children of Israel break the Sabbath?

Who is a true believer?

Say with me

You have heard of those of you that broke the Sabbath: We said to them: "You shall be changed into detested apes."(2:65)

Pray with me

Dear Allah, make me a true and a sincere believer of Islam.

The Prophet Sulayman ﷺ and the Ants

The Prophet Sulayman ﷺ (Solomon) was a just and wise king who ruled Jerusalem. He was the youngest son of the Prophet Dawud ﷺ. Like his father, he was a king and was also Allah's messenger. He was a humble man and a firm believer in Allah's power. Allah gave him great gifts and powers, which he used for the welfare of human beings by spreading Allah's message far and wide. He was always thankful to Allah for his guidance and gifts. The knowledge given to him by Allah included the ability to understand the language of animals, birds and insects. The birds were even part of his army. He was given control of the winds and his ships sailed across the seas in safety. The Jinns obeyed him and he would put them to different tasks. But nowhere did he cross the limits set by Allah. He ruled wisely and justly. His

wisdom was proverbial and his fame spread far and wide in the world. One day, the Prophet Sulayman ﷺ, who was marching with his army of Jinns, men, animals and birds, entered a valley inhabited by ants. Seeing the great force approaching them, one of the ants, frightened by the crowd of men and beasts so near the place they lived, said: "O ants, get into your dwellings, or Sulayman and his warriors might unknowingly march over you and crush you into the ground." (27:18) The Prophet Sulayman ﷺ could hear them and thanked Allah for this knowledge. He realized that Allah wanted him to be aware of the needs of even his lowest subjects so that no injustice was done to them, even unknowingly. The ever thankful Prophet Sulayman ﷺ praised and thanked Allah: "O Allah! Make me grateful to You for Your favours, which You have given me and my parents, and inspire me to do what is right to please You. And by Your Grace, admit me among Your righteous servants."(27:19) He was very grateful to Allah for giving him the opportunity to care for others and perform a good deed and earn His pleasure. Allah is most pleased when none of His creatures are ignored.

To the surprise of the ants, the great army moved away without harming even a single ant. The ants were very grateful to Allah and thanked him for taking care of them. Allah takes care of each and every creature of His and even responds to the prayers of the tiniest of His creatures.

Everything created by Allah lives its own life and indeed has the right to carry on with its life in a manner most suitable to its position in the world. Every creature has a task set by Allah to perform. Every single being in the universe helps to make the world run smoothly and for each there is a reward in the world to come.

Talk with me

What were the special gifts which the Prophet Sulayman ﷺ was blessed with?

What do we learn from this story?

Say with me

There is no creature on earth but Allah provides it sustenance. He knows its dwelling and its resting place. All is recorded in a glorious book. (11:6)

Pray with me

Dear Allah, make me like the Prophet Sulayman ﷺ, who even took care of the tiniest of creatures and respected the right to life of every being created by You.

Queen of Saba

One day, when the Prophet Sulayman ﷺ was inspecting his large army, he saw that the hudhud (hoopoe), a very wise bird, was not there. "Why is it that I do not see the hudhud? Is he not here? If he does not give me a good explanation for his absence, I will have him punished!"(27:20) After a while the hudhud came and excitedly informed him: "I am coming straight from the land of Saba (Sheba) and I have seen things there—a woman ruling the land! She is very virtuous and wise. She has a magnificent throne. I have never seen anything like it before. But she worships the sun instead of Allah and her people follow her. Satan has hidden the true path from them, and they have no guidance to turn to." (27:22-24)

The Prophet Sulayman ﷺ sent a letter inviting her to accept Islam. When the Queen of Saba discussed this letter with her council, they advised her to go to war. She did not agree, as she believed that war would just bring destruction. Instead, she sent some gifts to the Prophet Sulayman ﷺ, which he refused to accept. Then she went to Jerusalem to meet him. The Prophet Sulayman ﷺ asked a follower of his to bring her throne before she arrived to meet him. Some changes were made in it before she sat on it in the Prophet Sulayman's palace. She realized, however, that it was her own throne and was surprised by the power of the Prophet Sulayman ﷺ. When she was going to

enter the palace, she thought the floor was a lake of water. She lifted the edge of her garment and got ready to step into it. At this moment Prophet Sulayman ﷺ said, "It is but a palace paved with glass!" (27:44) The palace in fact was paved with slabs of transparent glass with water flowing beneath it. She exclaimed, realizing her mistake: "Lord, I have sinned against my soul. Now I submit with Sulayman to Allah, Lord of the Universe.' (27:44)

Indeed, things are not always what they appear to be. Some people see the true nature of things immediately, while others cannot see it at all, for the veil of ignorance screens the Truth from their eyes. However this is true only of this world. In the world of the Hereafter, all the veils will be removed and the true reality will show itself to all.

Talk with me

What did the hudhud tell the Prophet Sulayman ﷺ?

How did the Queen of Saba realize the truth of Allah?

Say with me

Satan has caused them to stray from the right path, so that they do not worship Allah, who brings forth what is hidden in the heavens and the earth, and knows what you hide and what you reveal. Allah! – there is no god but He! – Lord of the Throne Supreme!(27:25, 26)

Pray with me

Dear Allah, guide me away from ignorance and always enlighten me with the truth.

The Perfect Ruler

In the sixth century B.C. a great king, Dhul Qarnain, ruled over a vast kingdom which stretched from the Aegean Sea in the west to the river Indus in the east. He protected the weak and punished the unlawful. He possessed great power and equally great opportunities which he used to spread justice and righteousness. However, he believed that his power was given to him by Allah for the welfare of human beings. He gave the rich and the poor equal opportunities to be good and to do what was right. He did not interfere in the lives of people who were different from him and left them in peace. He was wise and tolerant to all kinds of people. He knew his own position and believed in living and letting others live.

One day Dhul Qarnain and his forces reached a valley between the mountains. The people who lived there were different from him and spoke a different language. They were peace-loving and hardworking. They told him about their problems and asked for his help. "O Dhul Qarnain! There is a tribe of Gog and Magog, who are our enemies. They invade our lands and cause great damage to our homes. We are ready to pay a tribute to you if you can somehow put up a wall between us and them." (18:94)

Dhul Qarnain was a true worshipper of Allah and knew that all his power came from Him, so he refused their offer of a tribute. He replied: "The power my Lord has given me is better than any tribute. Lend me a force of men, and I will raise a wall between you and your enemies." (18:95)

These people were skilled in melting iron and making all sorts of things out of it. It struck Dhul Qarnain that their skill could be turned to their advantage, so he ordered them: "Bring me blocks of iron." (18:96) He made them put the blocks of iron one atop the other, just like bricks, and in this way closed the gap between the two steep mountainsides. (18:94) When the iron blocks of the wall were red with heat, he said "Bring me molten brass so that I may pour it over them." (18:96) The wall, made of iron blocks and cemented with molten brass, presented a formidable sight and proved to be as formidable a barrier. The Gog and Magog people could neither climb over it, for it was as smooth and slippery as a sheet of glass, nor could

they dig through it, for it was harder than the rocks of the surrounding mountains. Never after that did Gog and Magog manage to invade their land.

In spite of all his efforts, Dhul Qarnain claimed no credit for himself. He said to them that it was Allah who had provided the ways and means by which they could be helped and protected. Before taking leave of them, the King pointed to the wall and, addressing the people, said: "This is a blessing from my Lord. But when the time comes, and the trumpet of the Last Judgement shall be sounded, He will make it crumble and turn into dust. Remember, every promise of the Lord is true." (18:98)

Talk with me
Why was Dhul Qarnain a perfect ruler?
Why did he not take credit for building the iron-wall?

Say with me
But whoever believes, and does good works shall have a rich reward, and by Our command, his task will be made easy. (18:88)

Pray with me
Dear Allah, guide me to be just and tolerant towards every human being. Allah, help me to work for the good of mankind.

The Quran Revealed

The Prophet Muhammad ﷺ was a very thoughtful person. Though he was a busy merchant he still took the time to think about Allah and His world. Every year, especially during the month of Ramdaan he would go into the cave of Hira, which was near the top of Jabal al-Nur, to think deeply. There he would ponder over the mysteries of creation. He would ask Allah for answers to the questions that troubled him: What is man's role in life? What does Allah require of us, as His servants? From where does man come, and where will he go after death?

In 610 A.D. during the month of Ramdaan, he had an extraordinary experience when he was all alone and deep in thought in the cave of Hira. The Angel Jibril came to him in human form and asked him to read. The Prophet trembled with fear and said he could not, as he was

unlettered. The Angel Jibril again asked him to read and he again declined. Asking him for the third time, Angel Jibril embraced him and said: "Read in the name of your Lord who created – created man from clots of blood. Read: Your Lord is the most Generous, who taught by the pen, taught man what he did not know."(96:1-5) These were the very first verses of the Quran that were revealed to the Prophet. He felt they were actually written in his heart. This experience made him scared and ill and he hurried back home. The fear he felt was natural. At home his wife Khadija consoled and encouraged him. Hearing her wise and soothing words, he felt very comforted.

After that for the next 23 years until his death in 632 A.D., he continued to receive revelations from Allah. The Prophet Muhammad ﷺ could neither make the revelations happen, nor stop them. They could happen at any time, whether he was sitting, riding a camel, talking, or even while he was giving a speech. These experiences always made him feel close to death, as if he was leaving his body and would never return. The Prophet once said, "Not once did I receive a revelation without thinking that my soul had been torn away." As soon as he received the revelation, he would narrate it to his companions, who would make a note of them. Then he would spread the message of Allah to others. The Quraysh did not like the message, as it went against their interests. To stop the spread of this message, they did everything possible, but we can see that they had no success.

When the Prophet Muhammad ﷺ went for his last Hajj, at that time the last Surah of the Quran was revealed to him. "Today I have perfected your religion and I have completed My blessings upon you, and I have approved Islam for your religion." (3:4-5) After praying, the Prophet spoke to his followers. He asked Muslims to let the Quran and his own example be their guides in life.

Talk with me

Who brought Allah's revelations to the Prophet Muhammad ﷺ and for how many years?
What did the Prophet say in his last speech to Muslims?

Say with me

We sent down the Book to you so that you should make clear to them those things in which they differ, and that it should be a guide and a mercy to those who believe. (16:64)

Pray with me

Dear Allah, I am very grateful and thankful to you for sending the Quran to us, a guide to show us how to conduct ourselves on this earth and earn our place in Paradise.

Friends of Today

The Quran friends have lots of friends today -- children just like you! Every day, children like you are learning more about Allah, His world, and His wonderful plan for this world. So what are you waiting for? Get ready to start exploring Allah's word, the Quran, with these stories of friends of today!

Allah's World

In the holidays, when Farah and Shuaib went to India, they took their children to Nainital, a hill station, for a week. The children, Hamza, Sidra and Sarah, enjoyed the trip and were very happy. The weather was cool and pleasant. They saw various ranges of the Himalayas, different lakes and many kinds of trees like pines, coniferous and oaks, and many also which bore fruit.

They enjoyed boating daily on the lake and had many picnics in the lush green forests at higher altitudes. They also went horse riding. The sight of the yellow-white, narcissi swaying in the breeze and their sweet fragrance were most memorable and breathtaking. In the forests they saw many birds, mainly pheasants, some small animals and also brightly coloured insects. They loved listening to the singing of the birds. They plucked fresh plums, figs, walnuts and many kinds of berries. They collected dry pine cones from the forest to take home. Little Sarah, plucked tiny, colourful, wild flowers and made a nice little bunch of them for her mother. Farah loved the bunch of flowers.

Farah and Shuaib also took the children to the neighbouring towns of Bhimtal, Saattal, Ranikhet and Kausani. It was a wonderful experience for them. They were very happy. It was the first time that they had been to the hills in India. They thanked Allah for creating such a beautiful world. Their parents told them that the world was not only beautiful but had been created with a purpose. All the things on this earth and in the universe have a purpose and they all work together, in accordance with Allah's wonderful plan. They also thanked Allah

for this wonderful experience that showed them how splendid their Creator was.

Talk with me

Where did Farah and Shuaib take their children?
How did the children feel at the end of the trip?

Say with me

Among the signs is the creation of the heavens and the earth, and the living things which He has spread out over them. If He will, he can gather them all together. (42:29)

Pray with me

Thank you, Allah, for creating such a beautiful and wonderful world, full of purpose, for us to live in.

Sharing with Friends

On Eid, Hamza, Sidra and Sarah got many gifts from their parents and other family members. They were very happy and thankful to Allah. Little Sarah saw some more clothes, books, toys and sweets in a separate box which had not been given to them. She was surprised and asked her mother, "Why have you not given these to us?" Her mother said, "They are not for you, but for your friends, Faizan, Kamran and Tayyaba." Naughty Sarah still wanted all the clothes, sweets and toys. Her mother explained, "We should not be selfish, but should share the gifts of Allah with everyone. Their parents do not have enough money to buy gifts for their children, so we got some gifts for them also. They are your friends and you should share your gifts and happiness with them." Sarah happily agreed and watched Sidra and Hamza wrap their gifts.

All three of them went to their friends' house in the evening. Faizan, Kamran and Tayyaba were delighted to get the gifts. Seeing their friends happy, Sidra, Hamza and little Sarah felt even happier. They thanked Allah for giving them this happiness, by having made them the means of their friends' happiness. Their mother told them that they should always share what they had with those who had nothing. Sharing and other kind acts please Allah a lot.

Talk with me

What did the children do on Eid?

What made them very happy?

Say with me

By no means shall you attain righteousness unless you give freely of that which you love: and whatever you give, Allah knows it well (3:92)

Pray with me

Thank you, Allah, for giving us so much. We are grateful to you, Allah, for guiding us to share things with others to bring them happiness and by doing so make ourselves happy too.

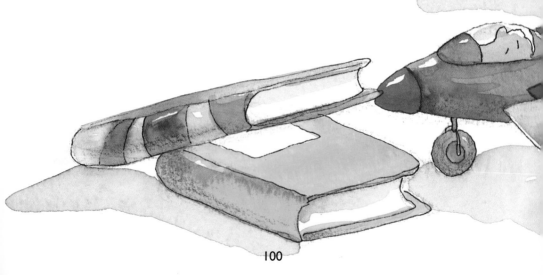

Football Match

Hamza had been working hard for almost a year after being selected for his class football team. He would reach school early in the morning for his football practice before the classes started. Hamza enjoyed playing football; he played as a centre forward.

During the football tournament's qualifying rounds, Hamza was to play in an important match. He was very happy and thankful to Allah for this opportunity. He also prayed for his team to win and to remove all his fears and worries. His family and friends were also excited and prayed for his and the team's success.

Sidra too could watch the match, as she studied in the same school. She enjoyed the match a lot. In the beginning, Hamza was not confident but, as the match progressed, he improved. Finally, it was Hamza's last-minute goal that won the match for his team. He was very happy and grateful to Allah. He knew that whatever good we do and get is all because of Allah's Grace. If one works hard and sincerely wants to do something, Allah helps one to achieve it.

Talk with me

Why was Hamza happy and worried at the same time?

Why was Hamza thankful to Allah?

Say with me
Victory comes only from Allah; Allah is mighty and wise. (8:10)

Pray with me
Dear Allah, thank you for making me
play well and win the match.
Thank you Allah, for
always being there
to help me.

Birds

Little Sarah was playing in the garden with her friends, Nathalie, Claire and Olivier. While climbing a tree, she saw a nest with three tiny chicks. Sarah was surprised to see such tiny birds with hardly any feathers. She felt worried about how they would survive.

In the evening she asked sensible Sidra about her fears. Sidra said, "Allah takes care of everyone. He will feed them and protect them and you should not worry about them." Sarah still wanted to take some food for the chicks and to bring them inside and cover them with a blanket. But Sidra stopped her and asked her to pray instead to Allah for their well-being.

Daily, Sarah would go and check up on them. Over the next ten days, they became stronger and noisier and would even flutter their wings. Sarah was surprised and very happy. She thanked Allah for taking care of them and making them beautiful and strong. Sidra said "Look, I told you that Allah would take care of them just as He takes care of all other creatures — Tigers, elephants, horses, lambs, rabbits, birds,

butterflies and the tiniest of insects. Allah is aware of everyone's needs, He loves us all."
The chicks grew and grew and when they became full-sized birds, they flew away.

Talk with me
Why was Sarah worried?
What did Sidra explain to her?

Say with me
Do they not see the birds that wing they flight in heaven's vault ? It is only Allah who sustains them up there. Surely in this there are signs for true believers. (16:79)

Pray with me
Dear Allah, thank You for taking care of all of us — human beings, big and small animals, little birds, colourful butterflies and tiny insects, in fact, all of nature.

Taking Care of Rukhsana Aapa

One day when Sidra, Sarah and Hamza were having breakfast, they realised that since morning they had not seen their maid, Rukhsana Aapa. Their mother told them that she was not well. She was suffering from high fever and so was resting in her room. Before leaving for their work, the parents asked the children to take care of Rukhsana Aapa.

The children were very happy with this responsibility. They decided to divide the work among themselves. Sidra went to Rukhsana Aapa's room, checked her temperature and helped her to the bathroom. Meanwhile Hamza made breakfast for her and his sisters helped her in taking it. After finishing their homework, they dusted and cleaned

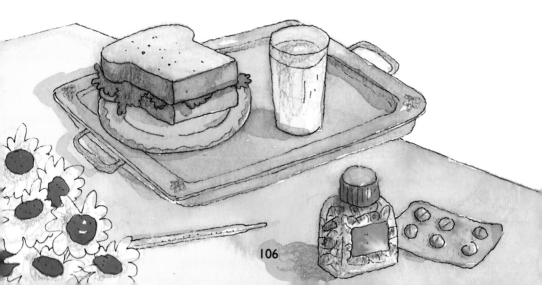

the house and also watered the plants. Then they sat with Rukhsana Aapa. Sidra massaged her head, Hamza read out stories to her and Sarah recited her poems. Rukhsana Aapa was very pleased. From time to time they checked her temperature, and gave her medicines and food.

With their love, care and medicines she soon got well and blessed the children. The parents were also happy with them. They told the children that Allah too would be pleased with them. They added that the Prophet Muhammad ﷺ had said that it was the duty of a Muslim to take care of the sick, even if that person was not a friend or a relative.

Talk with me

What made everyone happy?
Why should we take care of the sick?

Say with me

Not so the Lord of the Universe, who has created me; who gives me guidance, food and drink; who when I am sick, restores me; who will cause me to die and bring me back to life Hereafter; who, I hope, will forgive me my sins on the Day of Judgement. (26:82)

Pray with me

Thank you, Allah, for guiding us in helping and taking care of those who are ill.

Help for Tsunami Victims

The tsunami created havoc in countries like Indonesia, Thailand, Sri Lanka and the southern parts of India. It killed many people and destroyed their homes in a matter of a few minutes. Those who survived lost their loved ones, houses, money and everything else. Hamza asked his mother, "How can we help the victims of the tsunami?" His mother said, "We are already collecting money and useful items in the mosque; you can also do the same in your school."

The next day, Hamza and sensible Sidra, talked to their friends and also to the class teacher about helping the tsunami victims. The class teacher talked to the Principal, everyone agreed and so they excitedly started collecting money and useful items. The whole school started working for this noble cause. Hamza, Sidra and Sarah gave their monthly pocket money. When Hamza was taking out his old clothes, his mother suggested, "Give clothes and shoes which are in good condition, not the old and torn ones." The children understood this and gave only useful and good things. Finally, the school sent off a large amount of money and many useful items.

Later, in the same way, they helped people who had been affected by an earthquake in India and Pakistan and also the victims of the hurricane called Katrina in New Orleans. They thanked Allah for guiding them to do these good deeds.

Talk with me

What did Hamza want to do for the tsunami victims?
In what way did the children continue their good deeds?

Say with me

He that gives his wealth for the cause of Allah is like a grain of corn which brings forth seven ears, each bearing a hundred grains. Allah gives in plenty to whom He will; Allah is very generous and all-knowing. Those who give their wealth for the cause of Allah and do not follow their almsgiving with taunts and insults shall be rewarded by Allah; they shall have nothing to fear or to regret. (2:261, 262)

Pray with me

Dear Allah, we are very grateful to you for making us do good deeds by caring for our fellow human beings, especially when they are in trouble.

Neighbours

It was late in the evening and Hamza had not returned home. Farah got worried. Finally, when Hamza returned, she asked, "How could you be so irresponsible, and why have you come so late? You had to do work and then we were so worried!" Sarah and Sidra were scared and quiet.

Hamza said, "Mother, I am sorry for giving you trouble, but it was not because I was playing that I got late. Mrs Austin, our neighbour, asked me to get some groceries and milk, as she was not well, and there was no one at home to get these things. I had gone to the market to buy her what she needed." Farah regretted scolding him and said, "I am sorry, son, for unnecessarily scolding you. It is very good that you helped her. It is our duty to help our neighbours when they are in need. We should always be there for our neighbours." Farah hugged and kissed him. Hamza felt good and thanked Allah for guiding him to do what was right.

Later Farah and Sidra went to visit Mrs. Austin to inquire about her health and if any other help was needed. Mrs. Austin said that she would let them know if she needed them. She praised Hamza and was also very happy to spend time with them.

Talk with me

Why was Hamza late?

What is the duty of a Muslim towards his neighbours?

Say with me

Serve Allah and associate none with him. Show kindness to parents and kindred, to orphans and to the destitute, to near and distant neighbours, to those who keep company with you, to the traveller in need, and to your servants. (4:36)

Pray with me

Dear Allah, always guide me to help my neighbours and everyone else whom I can help.

Rain and Rainbow

One afternoon, it suddenly started raining. Hamza and Sidra were busy with their homework, but Sarah had none and was not even sleepy. She wanted to go out and play in the rain, but no one allowed her. When their maid, Rukhsana Aapa, went off to sleep, naughty Sarah secretly went out. She ran out into the garden. It was full of water and she enjoyed splashing and rolling around in it.

Seeing her having fun in the rain, her friends, Claire, Nathalie and Olivier, also joined her. They even brought balls and some paper boats. Together they had a very good time. They put the boats in the drains for a race, but very soon the boats got wet and torn. But nothing could dampen their pleasure.

After some time, the rain gradually stopped and the sun came out. With the coming of the sun, a huge bright rainbow spread across the

sky. Sarah and her friends felt it was beautiful and started counting the colours and announcing their favourites. Sarah thanked Allah for the beautiful rainbow, the colours, the rain and the sun and for making them have so much fun.

Then Sarah — the wet little monkey! – crept into her room, but when she sneezed, Rukhsana Aapa caught her there all wet and dirty. She scolded Sarah, and said that now she would surely fall ill. Sarah was scared and said sorry to her, while she changed her into some dry clothes.

Talk with me
How did Sarah have great fun?
Why did she thank Allah?

Say with me
It is He who sends down water from the sky, which provides you with your drink and brings forth the grass on which your cattle feed. And with it He brings up corn and olives, dates and grapes and fruits of every kind. Surely in this there is a sign for thinking men……(16:11-15)

Pray with me
Thank you, Allah, for creating the rain, the sun, and the colours of the rainbow and giving us so much fun.

Life after Rain and Rainbow

Sarah had a great time in the rain and looking at the rainbow was very exciting. But she went down with high fever because of getting wet. She felt miserable. She prayed to Allah that she would always obey her elders and would never play in the rain again. She hated being in bed and having so many medicines and having to eat such dull food. She also felt very sorry for her parents who were worried for her. She prayed to Allah to make her well just one last time and promised that she would never again do anything wrong.

Sarah could not go to school for the next three days and then it was a weekend. On the first two days, when she was very ill, Farah and Shuaib each took a day off from their offices. Her brother and sister tried to entertain her by reading out stories and talking about school. Hamza even told her about the football match in such detail that she felt as if she was there and, for a while, she even forgot her illness. Rukhsana Aapa made very nice soups for her. Everyone stayed around till she fell asleep and her mother slept with her in case she needed something during the night.

Soon she got better. She thanked Allah for giving her such a nice and loving family and also for creating good medicines. Sarah thanked everyone and promised to listen to them. They said they would always be there for her. She felt good. The little monkey got better and was soon up to her tricks, until Sidra reminded her of her promise to Allah not to be naughty and to obey her elders.

Talk with me
How did Sarah fall ill?
Why did she thank Allah?

Say with me
Those who surrender themselves to Allah and accept the true faith; who are devout, sincere, patient, humble, charitable and chaste; who fast and are ever mindful of Allah- on these, both men and women, Allah will bestow forgiveness and a rich reward. (33:36)

Pray with me
Dear Allah, thank you for giving me such a nice and loving family. Please, Allah, forgive my mistakes and always guide me to obey You and my elders.

Taking Care of the Old

Farah's uncle, Dr. Jamshed Khan, came to stay with her family. His son's family had gone to Spain for a few months. The children were very happy with him. They would accompany him for his walks in the evenings. The walks were very interesting, as he would tell them many interesting facts about the wonderful world created by Allah. He knew more than other people as he was a scientist.

One day Sarah asked her mother, "Why is Uncle Jamshed staying with us?" Farah replied, "He is our elder and he needs our help because he is old and his immediate family members are not there to take care of him." "But mother, he is so grown up and wise, why should he need our help?" "Little Sarah, in old age, one is surely wise, but uncle still needs others to take care of him due to his health. He has some physical problems because of his age, and he also needs company. Don't you enjoy being with him?" "Of course I do, I really like him. He tells us wonderful stories and also listens to our stories." Her mother went on, "He took care of us when we were children and now it is our duty to take care of him and to respect him. Allah loves those who take care of their elders." Sarah heard Uncle Jamshed asking for a glass of water and she ran to get water for him. Farah smiled, seeing Sarah's new found enthusiasm.

Talk with me

What did Sarah ask her mother?

What is our duty towards our elders?

Say with me

Allah has enjoined you to worship none but Him, and to show kindness to your parents. If either or both of them become old in your home, show them no sign of impatience, nor rebuke them; but speak to them kindly. Treat them with humility and tenderness and say: 'Allah, be merciful to them. They nursed me when I was an infant.' (17:23, 24)

Pray with me

Dear Allah, thank You for giving me this life, wonderful parents and relatives, and inspiring me to do deeds which please You, like taking care of others, especially our elders.

Sleep

Every night after having milk and brushing their teeth, the children waited eagerly for either of their parents, Farah or Shuaib, to tell them stories. They told them stories from the Quran and from the life of the Prophet Muhammad ﷺ. One day, Sidra was very tired after running in a race. She was scared that she might fall ill and miss her first quarterly exam. That night while listening to the story, she fell asleep.

After a good, deep sleep, she woke up the next morning, feeling fresh and healthy. She thanked Allah for the gift of sleep and ran to her mother happily. Her mother took Sidra in her arms and told her that Allah loves us and takes care of us. Everything that He has created is for our good and has a purpose. He has created sleep to give us rest and refresh us for the next day. This helps us to continue our work and play and be healthy. We have all come into this world with a purpose and sleep helps us to fulfill it by giving us timely rest.

Talk with me

Why was Sidra tired?
Why has Allah created sleep?

Say with me

Do they not see how We have made the night for them to rest in, and the day to give them light? Surely in this are signs for true believers. (27.86)

Pray with me

Dear Allah, we thank You for making us sleep, so that we are able to perform our duties in accordance with Your will.

Luck

Hamza and Sidra were worried because their quarterly exams had started. Little Sarah wished them the best of luck. Their father, Shuaib, who was going to drop them to school, asked Sarah while driving the car, "Why did you wish them luck?" Sarah was surprised and confused by his question. She replied, "Because with luck they will do well in their exam." Their father said, "This is not correct. Tell me, if they had not studied and worked hard, would they still perform well just because of luck?" At this they were quiet. Then he laughed and added, "It is so foolish even to think that luck can make any difference to the outcome of anything." He went on, "There is no substitute for the actual work you do. If You have to do well in an exam, you should go to school regularly, pay attention to what the teacher teaches, study at home and pray for Allah's Grace. The harder you work, the better the result."

All of them nodded their heads and Hamza said, "I think when we wish anyone luck, it is like a prayer to Allah." Sidra questioned, "How can that be? It is different." "Right," said their father smiling. "There is no such thing as luck. Instead, we should pray to Allah for His blessings, grace and guidance."

Sarah said, "Fine, I am going to pray to Allah that He does not let you forget what you have studied and guide you to do your exam well." All three of them learnt the very important lesson that one should depend only on Allah and one's own work. Now they felt relaxed and confident. Hamza and Sidra were not scared any more, because they had prayed to Allah and had also worked hard. Allah rewards everyone according to their work.

Talk with me
Why were Hamza and Sidra worried?
What important lesson did all of them learn?

Say with me
Blessed is the reward of those who labour patiently and put their trust in Allah. (29:59)

Pray with me
Dear Allah, always guide me to work hard for my needs and always bless me with Your Grace

Do not Trouble Others

Uncle Jamshed observed that generally during their walks Hamza either threw stones at stray dogs or plucked the leaves from the trees and plants for no particular reason. One day he asked him, "Hamza, why do you hit these dogs when they don't even trouble you? And why pluck leaves?" Hamza was surprised at this question, because he did all this quite thoughtlessly. "Just like that," he replied. "But this is bad. Firstly, you should not do anything thoughtlessly, when Allah has given you brains to think and guidance to decide what is right and wrong. Secondly, why trouble or hurt other living beings, who can feel pain and joy. It is a sin to hurt or trouble living beings created by Allah. They are just like us."

Hamza understood and felt bad about what he had been doing. He said he was sorry and would never again harm other creatures. Hamza said, "I know I was wrong. How would I feel if someone hit me, chased me or hurt me—and all for no reason?" His realisation pleased Uncle Jamshed a lot. Little Sarah said that now even she would not trouble butterflies or ants. Sensible Sidra said that she too would not pluck flowers or chase cats when there was no reason to do so.

Talk with me

What annoyed Uncle Jamshed?

What lesson did Uncle Jamshed teach the children?

Say with me

Pray to your Lord with humility and in secret. He does not love the transgressors. (7:56)

Pray with me

Dear Allah, always guide me not to commit the sin of hurting or troubling not only human beings but also all living beings.

Responsibilty

Hamza was very upset and scared because his father was not happy with him. He did not like Hamza having played truant from school just because his friends had done so. His father said, "Hamza, this is wrong. I never expected you to behave in such an irresponsible manner. The worst part is that you did something only because everyone else was doing it. That surely did not make it correct. You should think before you do or say something. You should do things which are right."

"How do we know what is right" asked Sarah. Before Shuaib could say anything, sensible Sidra explained, "That is easy. We should do

everything with accordance to Allah's will, and this is clearly explained in the holy Quran." Their mother walked in and said, "That's it. You should be responsible for what you do. What you do is what you will get in return. You will be punished or rewarded according to your deeds."

Their father continued, "If something important was taught in the class in your absence and later it came up in your exam, you would naturally score less in it. Would you tell your teacher that you got lower marks because of your friends, therefore their marks should be deducted instead of yours? And would she increase your marks because of the reason you gave? You know she would not do this. You have to be responsible for your acts and be ready to take the consequences. You just cannot shift your wrongs on to others, nor can you blame others for them. No one can share our burden or be responsible for our acts. We are rewarded for good deeds and are punished for bad deeds. It is as clear and simple as this." Hamza said that he was sorry and understood his mistake and would never do it again. He also said that in future he would act responsibly and only do what was correct.

Talk with me

Why was Hamza scared?
What did his parents say to him?

Say with me

Each man shall reap the fruits of his own deeds: no soul shall bear another's burden. In the end you shall all return to Allah, and He will resolve for you your disputes. (6:164) Allah will reward all men according to their deeds. He has knowledge of all their actions. Follow then the right path as you are bidden, together with those who have repented with you, and do not transgress. He is watching all your actions. (11: 111,112)

Pray with me

Dear Allah, forgive me for my mistakes and guide me to be responsible for all my actions and always do what is right. Thank you, Allah, for guiding me towards the correct path.

Shoes for Hamza

Hamza was quite desperate as he wanted a good pair of football shoes for the forthcoming inter-school football tournament and was not sure that his parents would buy them. He was worried that they were still upset with him for playing truant from school. Nor was he sure whether they would remember his shoes and he was too scared to remind them. So he prayed to Allah, because He is forgiving and answers our prayers.

One week before his match, when his parents returned after doing their regular shopping, he eagerly waited for the shoes and imagined them in the different packets which they had brought with them. He happily thought of getting the shoes. They opened a huge parcel which had groceries in it. In another one there were other household items.

In a pink one there was a white dress for Sidra and in a box there were some books.

He became sad and went out and sat on the lawn. Suddenly Shuaib came out and gave the box of shoes to him. He just could not believe that his parents had brought the shoes. They were exactly as he wanted, with yellow and green stripes. He was thrilled and hugged his father and thanked him for his love and concern. He thanked Allah for taking care of even his smallest of needs and giving him exactly the pair of shoes which he had wanted. Allah loves everyone and is aware of everything they need, however small. Allah is great.

Talk with me
What did Hamza want?
How do you know that Allah takes care of our smallest of needs?

Say with me
We have bestowed blessings on Adam's children and guided them by land and sea. We have provided them with good things and exalted them above many of Our creatures. (17:70)

Pray with me
Dear Allah, I know You love me and take care of all my needs and desires. No one can love and understand me more than You. Thank you, Allah.

Writing - A Gift of Allah

One day Sidra showed a short story she had written to her Uncle Jamshed. He was very impressed and said that she was blessed with talent, which was a gift from Allah. Sidra asked, "Is it a blessing that I can write stories?" Her uncle replied, "Yes, my child, it is a blessing. Not everyone can express their thoughts in writing. By means of writing you can communicate with many more people. Whatever good we have is a blessing from Allah, whether it be good food, clothes, a house, health, opportunities, intelligence or any kind of talent like writing," "I never thought of it this way, and now I am very thankful to Allah," said Sidra.

Her uncle went on, "If you have got a gift from Allah, you should not become proud but remain humble and share it with others. You should contribute to the well-being of other human beings." "But how can I do it by writing?" she asked. "You can do a lot by writing. You should write what is right. You can spread the message of Allah to help people to live by the will of Allah. You can help to improve people's lives. That would please Allah a lot." "This is wonderful, Uncle. Insha Allah, I will use my writing to spread Allah's message and make this life and the Hereafter better."

Talk with me
What impressed Uncle Jamshed?
What advice did he give to Sidra about her writing?

Say with me
He gives wisdom to whom He will; and he that receives the gift of wisdom is rich indeed. Yet none except men of sense bear this in mind. (2:269)

Pray with me
Dear Allah, thank You for Your many blessings, especially wisdom, and help me to use them to spread Your message for the well-being of mankind.

Thank you Allah

Farah and Shuaib were watching the news on the television and the children were having their dessert, when little Sarah started complaining to her mother that she had not been given enough dessert. Sidra asked her to keep quiet, but she would not and then Farah said, "You are such a thankless girl. Sidra and Hamza got even less and they are having it happily." Sarah went on, "But it was so little and I wanted more. Why did you not make more?" Farah said firmly, "Instead of thanking Allah for all that you have, you always complain. Do you know that there are so many children who do not even get two meals a day or a proper house to live in and they cannot even afford to go to school?" Sarah got scared and looked down.

Shuaib came to her and said, "Look, in the news you can see little children in India and Pakistan who have been affected by the terrible earthquake. They are out in the open in such cold weather without proper clothes and food. Some have been injured and many have even lost their parents. It was the same after the Katrina hurricane in New Orleans, or the tsunami which hit various countries earlier.

Otherwise also because of poverty children do not even get the basic needs. You have everything. You have parents to take care of you, a nice house, food, clothes, education and almost everything you want. You should thank Allah for His gifts to you. Come, all of you, and let's thank Allah." All three of them sat with their parents and thanked Allah for His many gifts.

Talk with me
What was Sarah complaining about?
What did her parents tell her?

Say with me
It was Allah who created the heavens and the earth. He sends down water from the sky with which He brings forth fruits for your sustenance. He drives the ships which, by His leave, sail the ocean in your service. He has created rivers for your benefit, and the sun and the moon, which steadfastly pursue their courses. He has given you everything you have asked for. If you reckoned up Allah's favours, you could not count them. Truly, man is wicked and thankless. (14:32-34)

Pray with me
Thank you, Allah, for taking care of me and giving me every worldly gift. I am very grateful to you. Dear Allah, bless me with a thankful nature

Calling Names

Saad and Aqsa, the children's cousins, came to stay with them for a weekend. One evening, while having cookies and milk, Saad told everyone about his mischief-making in the class. He told them how he and his friends made fun of their other class mates and secretly called them by funny names like fatso, monster and dumb head. He continued to talk badly about his friends and make fun of them.

Hamza, who did not like this, said "Why do you call them by such names?" Saad said, "Well, because they deserve these names. Like the one we call monster is really a big, dark, ugly boy and fatso is huge and round." Hamza said, "This is very bad. We should not make fun of others, because Allah does not like it. Everyone is created by the Almighty, so how can we make fun of any of His creations?"

Saad did not know what to say. Hamza continued, "One should never talk badly about others, especially when they are not present. That is back-biting. Allah does not approve of such acts. We should never do anything which He does not like." Saad was quiet and realized his mistake. He said, "I promise that from now on I will not do things which Allah does not like and I will also try to stop other friends of mine from doing so." He thanked Hamza for guiding him not to do wrong things.

Talk with me

What wrong things did Saad and his friends do?
What were the reasons which Hamza gave Saad to stop him behaving
as he did?

Say with me

Believers, let no man mock another man, who may perhaps be better
than himself. Let no woman mock another woman, who may perhaps
be better than herself. Do not defame one another, nor call one another
by nicknames. It is an evil thing to be called by a bad name after
embracing the true Faith. Those who do not repent are wrong- doers.
(49:11)

Pray with me

Dear Allah, make me a good child and don't let me make fun of others
or say bad things about them.

Compassion

Hamza took Saad for a friendly football match. Hamza's friend Ashley brought his brother Ted, who walked with a limp, to watch the match. Seeing him walk with a limp, Saad started giggling. When Hamza saw this, he did not like it at all. It became difficult for him to concentrate on his game, so he excused himself and went up to Saad. He took him aside and asked, "Why were you giggling?" "Don't be so stupid. Can't you see why I was laughing? In fact, how could you not laugh, seeing how Ted walked? My God, he was so funny!" He again started laughing and went on, "In our neighbourhood there is a blind man. Even he makes me laugh and I thoroughly enjoy troubling him. Nothing harmful, of course." Hamza was taken aback. "I cannot believe you can be so insensitive and heartless. In stead of being nice and compassionate, you are so mean and insensitive to them. Why should you laugh at them or trouble them? It was only two days back you promised that you would never make fun of others, and now you are doing something even worse! You are a hypocrite." Saad said in self-defence, "This is different. What's wrong with it? It's just harmless fun and they do look like idiots." Hamza said, "You should rather admire them. In spite of their handicaps, they are living respectable lives. I am not asking you to pity them, but to respect them and treat them normally. Allah does not approve of such behaviour." Later in the night, Saad went to Hamza and said that he genuinely realized his fault. He said sorry and promised that he would never again behave like this.

Talk with me
What made Saad laugh?
What did Hamza advise him to do?

Say with me
It is no fault in the blind, nor in one born lame, nor in one afflicted with illness... (24:61)

Pray with me
Dear Allah, guide me not to make fun of people who are differently abled or have any kind of handicap and make me show respect and compassion for all.

Science – Guidance from Allah

The children's cousin Namra came to stay with them for some weeks. She was a student of medicine. All the three children enjoyed talking to her and to hear her fascinating tales from the world of science. They were quite surprised to know that some years back people used to die of simple fever, chicken pox and tuberculosis, because there was no proper treatment. Namra explained, "With guidance from Allah, man has made great progress in every field and improved the quality of life." Sidra asked, "Now, not only can the heart be transplanted, but even other vital organs?" "Yes, that is true. The more you understand, discover and invent in science, the more you appreciate the creation of Allah. How the human body functions is amazing. Even for very simple acts, such intricate activities take place within body as only Allah can create. It is a miracle," said Namra.

Hamza said, "I think all sciences and their study are equally fascinating. They show what a magnificent Creator Allah is." Namra added, "You are right. It is thanks to Allah that our life has become so comfortable and easy. It is not only in the field of medicine, but see the train, planes, rockets, computer technology, weather prediction, and so on. Everything is a blessing from Allah. When we gain knowledge, we can appreciate Allah and His creation more and so worship Him better. To understand Allah and His world better, it becomes essential for every human being to be educated and seek knowledge." They enjoyed talking to her and asked her to tell them more about the fascinating world of Allah through science. This she continued to do until her stay came to an end.

Talk with me
What information surprised the children?
How does knowledge help us to understand Allah's world better?

Say with me
Allah, increase my knowledge. (20:114)

Pray with me
It is Allah who has guided us to acquire knowledge, which not only makes our life more comfortable, but also makes us understand Allah's world better. Thank you, Allah for guiding us.

Not to Laugh at Others Suffering

Sidra was standing with her friends Laiba and Armish in the school when they suddenly saw Afshan tumbling down the staircase. Laiba and Armish started giggling, because Afshan was not their friend. Sidra and some teachers who were passing by ran to help her. She was not seriously injured but only slightly hurt. The teachers took her for first-aid.

Sidra returned to her friends and scolded them. "How could you be so cruel and insensitive, laughing when someone was falling down and getting hurt?" Laiba said, "It was not 'someone', but Afshan, who is not our friend." Sidra did not like her argument and said, "It is not a question of friends and enemies, but of a fellow human being who was getting hurt, and instead of helping her you were laughing and enjoying her pain. This is cruel." Laiba became uncomfortable, then Armish said, "Afshan is not a good girl. She is always troubling others and she is also very proud. She deserves it. Allah must be punishing her." Sidra said, "How do you know whom Allah is punishing? This is wrong. Who are you to decide what she deserves? Fine, I agree that her behaviour is bad, but that does not mean that we should also behave like her. We should not enjoy others' suffering, whether they are our friends or not, and whether they are good or bad. I hope you understand this and will never behave like this again." Both of her friends felt bad and promised that they would never behave like this again. They prayed to Allah, asking for His forgiveness.

Talk with me

What did Laiba and Armish do when they saw Afshan falling down?
What did Sidra say to them?

Say with me

When you are blessed with good fortunes they grieve: but when evil befalls you they rejoice. (3:120)

Pray with me

Dear Allah, make me a good human being who is sensitive and not cruel to anyone, not even to enemies.

Allah Loves the Humble

One day Sidra's class teacher said, "It looks this year as if Sidra is going to be first in the class, because she is not only intelligent but is also sincere and hard working." Sidra was pleased and thanked Allah. During the games period Afshan, who always stood first, came to her and said arrogantly, "Don't take the teacher's remarks seriously, because no one can beat me. I am too good. At the most you will be able to get a second rank." Sidra was hurt, but said, "You are so proud. It is all in the hands of Allah. All we can do is just work hard." "I know it for sure, Sidra, that I will always come first, because I am so good. You can keep trying but it's hopeless," said Afshan proudly.

Sidra went away quietly and worked even harder. At the end of the term, she came first. She thanked Allah. She saw Afshan crying a lot. She went to her and said, "It is a sin to be proud. Even Satan was proud. Allah does not like the proud. You should be humble. All good comes from Allah, so why should you be proud?" Afshan said that she was sorry. Sidra added, "Ask Allah for forgiveness and correct yourself. You should stop being proud and always be humble. Pride only does damage. Whatever good we have is a blessing from Allah. Next time, maybe you will be first again. Just mend your ways."

Afshan stopped crying and prayed to Allah for His forgiveness and to guide her to the correct path. She also thanked Sidra.

Talk with me

What was Afshan's fault?

What happens in the end?

Say with me

Allah does not love the haughty, the vainglorious; nor those who, being mean themselves urge others to be mean also. He that gives no heed should know that Allah alone is self-sufficient and worthy of praise. (57:24)

Pray with me

Dear Allah, just never let me be proud or arrogant, because that is what Satan is like. Guide me towards humility.

Always be Polite

One night after Farah had finished reading stories to the children from the lives of prophets, Sidra said that she wanted to tell her about their trip with Mr. and Mrs. Ahmed's family. Sidra said, "Mr. and Mrs. Ahmed are elders and we should respect and obey them, but Mother, they behaved very oddly, and I think they were quite wrong." Farah became worried and asked her what had happened. Before answering her, Sidra asked another question, "Is it all right to shout at and insult a beggar when you don't want to give him alms, or even when you are giving it?" Farah said not at all. Sidra said that this was what she had seen them doing. Farah was quite shocked. Sidra went on, "Not only

that, but they were quite rude with the driver and the receptionist."
Sarah added, "Did you forget how they scolded and insulted a waiter
when we went out for lunch?" Sidra said, "Yes, Sarah is right. All these
people were very hurt. We didn't like it one bit. You have always asked
us to be polite and I think elders too should be polite!" Farah nodded
and said, "Absolutely. We should never insult any other human being.
We should be polite and soft spoken to everyone, whether young or
old, rich or poor. It is not good to be angry or rude with others. Allah
dislikes such behaviour."

Talk with me
What did Sidra tell her mother?
What was Farah's advice to her children?

Say with me
Allah does not love harsh words, except when uttered by a man who is
truly wronged. Allah hears all and knows all. Whether you do good
openly or in private, whether you forgive an injustice-Allah is forgiving
and all-powerful. (4:48)

Pray with me
Dear Allah, make me behave politely and nicely with everyone. Never
let me get angry. Thank you, Allah.

Just make Friends

On their way back from the mosque after evening prayers, Hamza told his father, Shuaib, about his classmate, Yunus's fracture. His father asked, "Did you go to see him?" "No, I did not, he is the captain of the rival football team and he is not my friend. He is always troubling me." "Son, this is not good," replied his father. But Hamza went on, "No, father, he is really bad. He plays unfairly, he cheats and he even hits me. I think he hates me and I hate him too. He is my enemy." Shuaib said, "I still say you are wrong. If someone is bad to you, it does not mean that you too should become bad. You should answer his bad deeds with your good deeds. This would show him the correct way. One does not do good deeds only in response to others' good deeds, but because Allah asks us to do so in all circumstances. This pleases Allah. Tomorrow you had better visit him and start being nice to him. I am sure he will then become better and you will become friends." Hamza promised his father that he would change his ways and would surely visit him.

A fortnight later, one day Hamza brought a friend to meet his parents and it was Yunus. His parents were very pleased with his effort. Later Hamza told them excitedly, "Father, I did exactly as you asked me to do and after some time Yunus also changed his ways and even said sorry to me. We are still captains of rival teams, but we are also good friends."

Talk with me

Why did Hamza not go to visit Yunus though he was ill?
How did Yunus become Hamza's friend?

Say with me

Good deeds and evil deeds are not equal. Return evil with good, and he who is your enemy will become your dearest friend. But none will attain this attribute save those who patiently endure; none will attain it save those who are truly fortunate. (41:34, 35)

Pray with me

Dear Allah, thank You for guiding me to make even enemies my friends. Make me always do good deeds, whatever the circumstances.

Why Discipline?

Sitting on her mother's lap little Sarah asked, "Why do we have to reach school in time? I mean, if we are late by an hour or so, what is the problem?" Her mother kept smiling and listening to her as she went on, "Why do we have to follow rules in school? Why so much strictness at home? Mother, you keep telling us do things in time and according to one rule or the other Why so much of discipline? Why can't I get up when I want to, or play and study as I want to?" "Have you finished asking questions?" her mother asked. Sarah nodded her head. "Well, Sarah, have you seen the sun coming out from the west sometimes or coming out at night according to its mood? Do you see that it is sometimes cold in December and sometimes warm? The seeds take particular time for sprouting and so does the birds and animals and even we human beings to grow. Do we sometimes eat from our noses instead of our mouths?"

Sarah interrupted and said that school was different. Her mother went on, "Okay, let's talk about your school. If all of you started coming to school at different times would it be possible to have any classes or for that matter, if the periods were not fixed, how would it be decided when to study mathematics and when English, or when to play. What about roads? If there were no traffic rules, would it be possible to drive? My little angel, if there was no discipline, there would be confusion and therefore the world would come to a standstill. To be able to work smoothly, the world of nature follows a discipline according to the will of Allah. We should do the same. Discipline is essential for the world to run properly. It is necessary to achieve our goals and fulfill the purpose of our lives on this earth." Sarah thanked her mother for answering all her questions and making her see the truth.

Talk with me

What were Sarah's complaints?

Do you agree with her complaints? Why?

Say with me

It was to reveal the truth that He created the heavens and the earth. He caused the night to succeed the day and the day to overtake the night. He made the sun and the moon obedient to Him, each running for an appointed term. He is the Mighty, the Gracious One. (39:5)

Pray with me

Dear Allah, thank You for teaching us the importance of discipline.

Only Need not Greed

Everyone was having lunch one Sunday. Sarah had heaped up more food on her plate than she could eat, so she started whispering to Sidra and Hamza to take some from her, because she knew that her parents did not like any kind of wastage. Shuaib saw that she was feeling bad, so he asked her to keep whatever was left and finish it in the evening. Sarah felt relieved. Her father said, "This time I did not say anything, as I saw that you had realized your mistake. Just make sure that you do not repeat it." She promised that she would never do it again.

Shuaib went on, "We should not be greedy and should take only what is needed and not waste anything. There are so many children all over the world and also elders who do not even get regular meals and so we should not waste any food. Allah created this world for all of us and we should share the resources given by Him and not waste them. It is not only food I am talking about, but everything that we get from Allah." Sidra asked, "What all? Is it nature around us — trees and so on?" Their father said, "Yes, that is what I meant. We should not ruin Allah's world due to our greed and excesses. Whether it is food, trees, water, land, minerals, oil, gas or other such things in the environment, we should not use them excessively. It is for everyone. Excess usage can destroy the balance of the world as created by Allah and so bring destruction and havoc to the world, like floods, earthquakes and other natural disasters. Already human greed has destroyed a lot on this earth. We should take what we need not what we greed."

Farah joined them and said, "You know, the Prophet Muhammad ﷺ was against the cutting of green trees unnecessarily, even during war. He forbade destroying trees, crops and animals. He said that one who planted a tree or grew crops to feed people, birds and animals, would receive rewards for almsgiving." All three of them promised that they would never be

greedy and would not waste Allah's gifts.

Talk with me

Why is it wrong to waste food?
What did Shuaib ask them to do?

Say with me

Do not squander your substance wastefully, for the wasteful are Satan's brothers; and Satan is ever ungrateful to his Lord. (17:27)

Pray with me

Thank you, Allah, for creating a wonderful world. Guide us to take care of it and not destroy it with our greed and excesses.

Giving Others their Due

The next day, after dinner, Farah said, "Children, yesterday your father was telling you why it is important not to be greedy and to share all nature's gifts with others. Tonight I want to explain to you that it is not only natural resources, but also man- made things and what all we earn that we should share with others."

Little Sarah asked, "How can we do that? We don't live together with everyone in the same house and so we can't eat together." Sensible Sidra said, "You are always in a hurry to ask questions. Just wait and listen to mother." Their mother smiled and said, "You needn't live together in the same house to do this and it is not just about food. Look, all are not same. Our circumstances are not simillar." "Mother, I don't understand," said Sarah again. Farah explained, "Some of us are educated, some are not, some are rich and others are poor. It becomes the duty of the educated to teach or help one who is uneducated and for the rich to share their money and the facilities which can be bought with it with the poor. Whatever we have is a gift from Allah, so it becomes our duty to share it with the others who live on this earth with us and who are less fortunate. We should also take care of those who are weak, like the poor, orphans and even animals. There are many who will not even ask for help, but we should be sensitive enough to realize their need and help them in whatever ways we can."

Hamza asked, "Does it mean we have to do this regularly?" Farah said, "Absolutely, it has to be done regularly. A fixed amount has to be taken from our income for the poor every month. It could be given once a year though. It is called Zakat. We have to be responsible for the well-being of others too who do not have means to take care of themselves. We should not be greedy, but always ready to share."

Talk to me

What did Farah want to explain to the children?

Why is it important to share what we have with our fellow human beings?

Say with me

Believers, bestow in alms a part of what We have given you before that day arrives when commerce and friendship and intercession shall be no more. Truly, it is the unbelievers who are unjust. (2:254)

Pray with me

Dear Allah, guide me to help those whom I can and make me share with others all the blessings You have given to me.

Do not Tell Lies

Laiba, a friend of Sidra rang her up. She was quite worried and said, "I am in trouble I want your advice." Sidra also became worried, hearing her sound so troubled. Laiba went on, "In mathematics I got very low marks, but at home I lied to my mother that I had got good marks." Sidra was taken aback and said, "How could you lie and that also to your parents? It is unbelievable!"

Laiba became uncomfortable and said, "I am sorry and feeling very bad. I was scared that my parents would get hurt." "This is so stupid! As if now, when they would come to know, they would be happy! You have made things worst with your lie. Now they will be more hurt. One cannot hide a lie forever. What about Allah? Were you not worried about Him? He does not like liars. One lie leads to more lies and more wrong doings", said Sidra. "You are right, Sidra. When my class teacher asked me to bring my parents, I lied to her that my mother was not well and my father was not in town. Now next week my parents will be going to school and they will surely come to know. I am very scared. What shall I do?" asked Laiba. Sidra said, "What is there to ask? You should tell them the truth." Laiba was terrified and said, "No, there is no way that I can tell them the truth I am very scared of them. They will never forgive me." Sidra went on, "Don't be scared. Tell them the truth and ask for their forgiveness. They will surely pardon you, if you promise never to lie to them again. Ask Allah's forgiveness also."

The next evening, Laiba thanked Sidra for her advice. She told her that her parents had forgiven her. She hoped that Allah would also pardon her. She said that she would work hard at her studies and would never lie again.

Talk with me
What wrong did Laiba do?
What advice did Sidra give her?

Say with me

Shall I tell you on whom the devils descend? They descend on every lying sinner. They eagerly listen, but most of them are liars. (26:221-223)

Pray with me

Allah is most compassionate, merciful and forgiving. Dear Allah, forgive me for all my wrongs and guide me to do what is right. Please, Allah, never let me lie to anyone.

Hope, Patience and Prayer

Sidra was quite upset and sad. For the last few months, she had been sending stories and essays to some children's magazines, but not even one had been published. She felt disheartened and decided that she would never write again or even if she did write, she would never send what she wrote for publishing.

When her mother saw her sad and disheartened, she had a talk with her. She said, "Why are you so heartbroken? The rejection should not discourage you. It should encourage you rather to try to write better. You should honestly analyse what are your weak points and then work on them." Sidra said, "But mother it is pointless. I have lost hope that my writings will ever be published." But her mother went on, "Allah does not like those who give up hope. We should always be hopeful. You should be patient and pray to Allah and continue to write. You should not give up

Goodnight Stories from the Quran

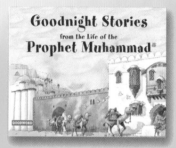

Goodnight Stories from the Life of the Prophet Muhammad

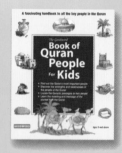

A fascinating handbook to all the key people in the Quran

The Goodword Book of Quran People For Kids

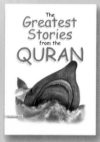

The Greatest Stories from the QURAN

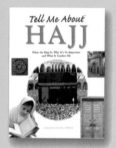

Tell Me About HAJJ

What the Hajj Is, Why It's So Important and What It Teaches Me

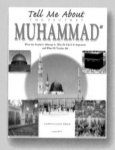

Tell Me About THE PROPHET MUHAMMAD

What the Prophet's Message Is, Who He Was & Is Important and What He Teaches Me

Parent's Love and other Islamic Stories

Madinah Arabic Reader Book 1

EIGHT PART COURSE FOR THE LEARNING OF ARABIC AS TAUGHT AT THE ISLAMIC UNIVERSITY, MADINAH

Dr. V. Abdur Rahim

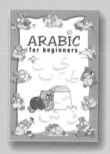

ARABIC for beginners

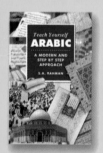

Teach Yourself ARABIC

A MODERN AND STEP BY STEP APPROACH

S.A. RAHMAN

Arabic Conversation Book

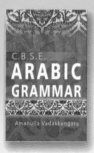

C.B.S.E. ARABIC GRAMMAR

Amanulla Vadakkangara

Let's Speak Arabic

Learn Arabic Conversation in just one week!

S.A. Rahman

Spoken Arabic MADE EASY

AMANULLA VADAKKANGARA

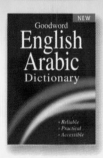

NEW

Goodword English Arabic Dictionary

• Reliable
• Practical
• Accessible